Christmas in Canada

PAPERBACK ISBN 0-460-90553-8
HARDBOUND ISBN 0-460-90552-X

PRINTED IN CANADA

DESIGNED BY LESLIE SMART MTDC FRSA FSIA

ILLUSTRATED BY FRANK DAVIES MTDC MSIA

MARY BARBER & FLORA McPHERSON

Christmas
in Canada

THE EARLY DAYS

FROM SEA TO SEA

SPIRIT OF CHRISTMAS PAST

SPIRIT OF CHRISTMAS PRESENT

J . M . DENT & SONS (CANADA) LTD.

TORONTO

Foreword

Not all Canadians have been pioneers, yet the pioneering spirit has given a special quality to the Canadian Christmas. Dickens in a cold town hall, mummers on the streets of St. John's, an angel in cheesecloth at a school concert, a carol sung by the Hurons—it's an old story in a new setting. On Christmas day in the Klondike a suit of long woollen underwear wrapped a new-born baby; at Lake Tetana, B.C., with the temperature sixty degrees below zero, the newest in packaged foods provided modern pioneers with Christmas dinner; in the Arctic, flaming oil drums signalled planes delivering Christmas mail.

Cynics and complainers there have been, lamenting what Canadians have done to Christmas. So it must always be, for the festival is part of the people. The noisy shopping districts of modern cities take their place with the revelry of the fur traders, the solemn *fête de noel,* the home-made gaiety of settlements. For a Czech family, the Christmas decorations in the Union Station meant the same renewal of faith as Champlain had found in the midnight mass of the little Quebec church three centuries before. The eternal miracle has been adapted by Canadians to their own place and time. Of their records we have made this book.

MARY BARBER
FLORA MCPHERSON

Acknowledgements

★ ★ ★ ★ ★ ★ ★ ★ ★ ★ ★ ★ ★ ★ ★ ★ ★ ★ ★ ★

Thanks are due to the following for permission to use material from the works named:

James Bannerman, 'A Victorian Innovation' (original title: 'Christmas in Canada 100 Years Ago'), *Chatelaine*, December, 1955. *The Beaver*, 'Christmas in the Fur Trade,' December, 1941. Morley Callaghan and The Canadian Bank of Commerce, 'The Bachelor's Dilemma' by Morley Callaghan. Gregory Clark and Canada Wide Feature Service, 'Social Engineering' by Gregory Clark. Edgar Andrew Collard, 'Christmas Shopping in 1876,' *Montreal Gazette*, December 25, 1948. T. Eaton Co., for source material for 'The Santa Claus Parade' by Margaret Munnoch. Robert Finch, 'The Crib,' *Saturday Night*, December 27, 1952. John Fisher, 'Christmas Customs' (original title: 'Christmas in Canada Whose-Which?'), *John Fisher Reports*, CBC, Christmas, 1949. Foster Advertising Ltd., 'Brébeuf's Legacy' (original title: 'Canada's First Christmas Carol'), *Forward with Canada—1948*, Northern Electric Co. Ltd. *Globe & Mail*, 'Contractual Goodwill' (original title of editorial: 'Contractual Christmas'), July 28, 1954. The Grenfell Association of America, 'How Santa Claus Came to Cape St. Anthony' from *Off the Rocks* by Wilfred T. Grenfell, Philadelphia, Sunday School Times. Mrs. F. P. Grove and McClelland & Stewart, 'Dawn and Diamonds' from *Over Prairie Trails* by Frederick Philip Grove. E. C. Guillet, 'In the Days of Champlain' (original title: 'Christmas among Our Pioneers'), *School*, December, 1947. Houghton Mifflin Co., 'For the Yuletide Feast' from *Curtain Time* by Ruth Harvey. Dr. Nadine Hradsky, 'Our First Canadian Christmas' by Dr. Nadine Hradsky, *Maclean's*, December 15, 1954. Little, Brown & Co., 'Frostbound, 1937' from *Driftwood Valley* by Theodora C. Stanwell-Fletcher. *The London Free Press*, 'Yuletide Sport' by James Anthony, December 21, 1940. Longmans, Green & Co. (Toronto), 'When Heaven Smiled on Our World' from *Laurentian Heritage* by Corinne Rocheleau Rouleau. *Maclean's*, 'Louis Riel's Joke' by R. P. Ottewell, December 15, 1937. Hugh MacLennan and Wm. Collins Sons & Co., 'An Orange from Portugal' from *Cross Country* by Hugh MacLennan. The Macmillan Co. of Canada Ltd., 'A Cricket Singing' from *A Naturalist in Canada* by Dan McCowan; 'Boarder's Christmas' from *Landfall* by Lieut.-Commander Frederick B. Watt. McClelland & Stewart Ltd., 'Hoodoo McFiggin's Christmas' from *Literary Lapses* by Stephen Leacock. Mr. Horace B. McClung and Thos. Allen Ltd., 'First Days in Manitoba' from *Clearing in the West* by

Nellie McClung; 'An Evening with Dickens in Manitou Town Hall' from *The Stream Runs Fast* by Nellie McClung. McGraw-Hill Ryerson Ltd., 'Yule Logging' from *Sense and Nonsense* by Eric Nicol, Ryerson Press, and 'Edna Eldorado' from *I Was There* by Edith Tyrrell, Ryerson Press. *Montreal Star*, 'Jacques Cartier, 1535'. Harold Ober Associates Inc., 'Anticipation' and 'The Concert' from *The Mountain and the Valley* by Ernest Buckler, copyright 1952 by Ernest Buckler. *The Ottawa Journal*, 'St. Nick Flies the Oil Flare Trail' by John Dalrymple, January 24, 1952. Mrs. R. J. Renison and British Book Service (Canada) Ltd., 'Magi on Snowshoes' (original title: 'Indian Christmas') from *One Day at a Time* by Rt. Rev. R. J. Renison. *The Winnipeg Free Press*, 'King for a Meal,' December 24, 1947.

SOURCES

Sir Richard Henry Bonnycastle, *Newfoundland, 1842*, Vol. 2: 'In Newfoundland, 1842.' Samuel Hearne, *A Journey from Prince of Wales' Fort in Hudson's Bay to the Northern Ocean in the Years 1769, 1770, 1771, and 1772*: 'Travelling to the Northern Ocean'. John Howison, *Sketches of Upper Canada*: 'Reverie'. *Jesuit Relations*: 'Midnight Mass at Quebec, 1645' and 'Father Jean Enjalran Writes from St. Ignace, 1679'. Catherine Parr Traill, *The Backwoods of Canada*: 'Pioneer Celebrations.'

Contents

▲ ♦ ▲ ♦ ▲ ♦ ▲ ♦ ▲ ♦ ▲ ♦ ▲ ♦ ▲ ♦ ▲ ♦ ▲ ♦ ▲ ♦ ▲ ♦

THE EARLY DAYS

FROM SEA TO SEA

The Early Days

Jacques Cartier, 1535

★ ★

The first Christmas observed in Canada, that of 1535, was kept—but scarcely enjoyed—by one hundred and ten souls in a tiny palisaded fortress on the banks of the Ste. Croix River (now the St. Charles), near the present City of Quebec. On the site of the latter was then the Indian Village of Stadacona.

Jacques Cartier and his advance guard of settlers were by Christmas time beginning the struggle with the terrible hardships which during the winter beset the little band, killed twenty-five of its members, and reduced the remainder to a state of helplessness for many weeks.

The French ships had come bravely up the river during the previous summer, and had been joyously welcomed by the Indians, who were well supplied with gifts by the newcomers. The Isle of Bacchus (the Island of Orleans) and the land on either side of the great river of Canada had been explored, and a plot of land at the mouth of the Ste. Croix had been selected as the most suitable location for winter settlement. Jacques Cartier had made his way up as far as Hochelaga, and had returned to his band in time to over-see the final preparations for the cold weather.

It became noticeable before winter set in that there was a change of attitude on the part of the Indians. Outwardly they were friendly, but the Frenchmen soon became convinced that the two guides, whom they had carried off to France on a previous expedition and had brought back to serve as interpreters, were sowing disaffection among the people of Stadacona. Their influence on Chief Donnacona was marked, and the settlers took as their motto thenceforward, 'He who is watchful loses nothing.'

By the end of November the ships were frozen in and the little colony was beginning to discover the weak points in the winter preparations. The buildings could not keep out the penetrating cold. There were no cellars in which to keep supplies. All the drinkables were frozen hard, and melted snow had to be used for water, as rivers and streams were soon locked fast by the ice. Salt meat and stale vegetables formed the greater part of the diet, and by Christmas time health was beginning to suffer and the first whisper of the dread disease of scurvy was apparent among the whites.

The Indians hovered round, always watching. Sometimes they came to visit the settlement, and often they tried to entice the whites to visit their village on one pretext or another. There were ceremonious protestations of friendship on both sides, but the French were always conscious of the silent and observant movements of the natives. They, therefore, determined, above all, no matter how sick they were, to maintain a show of activity and strength about the fortress, lest, tempted by the obvious weakness of the garrison, the Indians should decide to attack it.

Christmas in those circumstances couldn't be a very merry affair. It came, however, before the worst of the winter trials, while the settlers were still buoyed up by the hope of future discoveries and by the tales of Donnacona—a man of some imagination, apparently—who told them of precious stones and metals to be found in lands beyond the country of Saguenay; of white men dressed in cloth like themselves who inhabited a region near a great inland sea of fresh water; of lands of luxurious vegetation south of the Great River, where other red-skinned people lived; and of a mysterious race of one-legged people living in some ill-defined territory far from the district known as Canada. All these things interested the adventurers mightily, and imagination, combined with a taste of the most precious of their food supplies, probably helped to make Christmas Day a little more cheerful than those which had preceded it. It was certainly far more cheerful than many which followed it, for there came a time when all but ten of the party were near death from scurvy. Courageous hearts alone enabled the little colony to hold out until the spring, and to deceive the Indians into thinking the band strong and prepared for attack in the days when they were threatened with utter extermination.

THE MONTREAL STAR

In the Days of Champlain

Perhaps the earliest Christmas celebration in Canada was at Saint Croix or Port Royal, in Nova Scotia, in the early years of the seventeenth century; but we have the details of one at Quebec a few years later in Champlain's lifetime. At the feast the seignior and his lady were seated in rough chairs at the head of a long table which stretched the full length of the main room of the log manor-house. Ranged below them were lesser persons on crude benches. There was but little silver plate in those days, but squares of birchbark and Indian bowls of polished basswood served the same purpose. Everyone carried his own knife; there were no forks, but bark spoons were provided.

The feast had the tang of another age. There were cakes of corn bread, great kettles of eels, salmon, and beans all boiled together and served in the bowls. Then the same bowls were filled with a rich meat soup thickened with pounded nuts. Corn, peas, and baked squash formed the next course, and then, after the appetizers, came the *pièce de résistance*. Great joints of roast venison were carved up, and deep squirrel pies were served; and there were baked wild pigeons, partridges, blackbirds, and owls, usually all together. For the dessert there were cakes of maple sugar and a sweetmeat compounded of nuts and sunflower seeds, with a sauce made of dried berries and boiling water.

E. C. GUILLET

Brébeuf's Legacy

ᏍᏍᏍᏍᏍᏍᏍᏍᏍᏍᏍᏍᏍᏍᏍᏍᏍᏍᏍᏍᏍᏍᏍᏍᏍᏍᏍᏍᏍᏍᏍᏍᏍᏍ

A midsummer morning and the sun a glitter of gold on the far-spreading St. Lawrence. From beneath the grey rock of Quebec a small fleet of canoes glides out on the broad shining river. There, among the bronze-skinned Hurons, his arms swinging his paddle in steady rhythm, sits a man in the jet-black robe of the Jesuit Order. On this July morning, 1626, Father Jean Brébeuf is setting out to carry the Cross into the wilderness of Canada.

Against the mighty current of the St. Lawrence, Brébeuf and the Hurons drive their canoes ever onward . . . up the Ottawa, past the white fury of raging falls and rapids . . . across to Georgian Bay, through a maze of blue lakes and rivers . . . and, at last, after weeks of toil and danger, to the western shore of the Bay of Penetanguishene. There, in the Indian village of Toanche, Father Brébeuf begins the first Jesuit mission in the land of the Hurons.

For twenty-three years he labours and suffers to bring the light of the Faith to these Indian savages. At the end of that time the crosses of twelve Christian missions are raised among Huronia's white-pine forests. But just as the harvest seems richest in promise, a black cloud appears on the horizon. Like a violent whirlwind, sweeping all before it, the dreaded Iroquois burst upon the trembling Hurons!

One after another the outlying missions are fired by the Iroquois, the Hurons in hundreds tortured and slaughtered. As the enemy approaches Father Brébeuf's mission, the Hurons beg him to fly to safety. But in this hour of danger he refuses to stir, and, when the Iroquois break through the wooden palisades, they find him there, comforting the wounded and dying. Tied to a stake by his jeering captors, Brébeuf suffers the cruelest of torments with sublime and unsurpassed fortitude. At last, when his body can endure no more, this noble servant of God wins for all eternity the crown of martyrdom.

But the martyrdom of Jean Brébeuf has not been in vain. His heroic example has continued to inspire Christian missionaries through the course of three centuries. Even the words of Brébeuf live on. Among the remnant of Hurons who escaped destruction there were those who remembered a Christmas carol, written by Brébeuf in the Hurons' own language . . . Canada's first Christmas carol . . . 'Jesus Ahatonhia' . . . 'Jesus is Born!'

> 'Twas in the moon of winter time when all
> the birds had fled,
> That Mighty Gitchi Manitou sent angel
> choirs instead.
> Before their light the stars grew dim, and
> wand'ring hunters heard the hymn
> 'Jesus, your King, is born; Jesus is born; in
> excelsis gloria!'

—And it came to pass, as the angels were gone away from them into heaven, the shepherds said one to another, 'Let us now go even unto Bethlehem, and see this thing which is come to pass, which the Lord hath made known unto us.' And they came with haste and found Mary, and Joseph, and the babe lying in a manger!

> Within a lodge of broken bark the tender
> Babe was found,
> A ragged robe of rabbit skin enwrapped His
> beauty round.
> And as the hunter braves drew nigh, the
> angels' song rang loud and high;
> 'Jesus, your King, is born; Jesus is born; in
> excelsis gloria!'

—Now when Jesus was born in Bethlehem of Judaea in the days of Herod the King, behold, there came wise men from the east to Jerusalem, saying, 'Where is he that is born King of the Jews? for we have seen His star in the east, and are come to worship Him.'

5/ *The Early Days*

The earliest moon of winter time is not so
round and fair
As was the ring of glory on the helpless
Infant there.
And Chiefs from far before Him knelt with
gifts of fox and beaver pelt.
'Jesus, your King, is born; Jesus is born; in
excelsis gloria!'

'Fear not, for behold, I bring you good tidings of great joy, which
shall be to all people. For unto you is born this day in the city of David a
Saviour, which is Christ the Lord.'

O children of the forest free, O sons of
Manitou,
The Holy Child of earth and heav'n is born
to-day for you.
Come kneel before the radiant Boy, Who
brings you beauty, peace, and joy.
'Jesus, your King, is born; Jesus is born; in
excelsis gloria!'

FORWARD WITH CANADA—1948

Midnight Mass at Quebec, 1645

The first stroke of the midnight mass rang at eleven o'clock, the 2nd, a little before the half-hour; and then they began to sing two airs—*Venez mon Dieu*, etc., and *Chantons noe*, etc. Monsieur de la ferté sang the bass; St. martin Played the violin; there was also a german flute, which proved to be out of tune when they came to the Church. We had finished a little before midnight; they nevertheless sang the *Te Deum*, and a little later a cannon shot was fired as the Signal of midnight, when mass began; the bread was blessed when the priest went to open his book. This was the 1st bread blessed for several years, during which it had been stopped, on account of the precedence in its distribution which everyone claimed. The renewal of the custom was caused by the devotion of the toolmakers, whose devotion urged them to have it during midnight mass; and people's minds were disposed to restore this custom. Monsieur the Governor received the chanteau*, that he might furnish it on the Sunday following: what was done to obviate the complications of the preferences claimed was, to order that after a portion had been given to the priest and to the Governor, all the others should receive as they might come and chance to be in the Church: beginning now in front, and now in the rear.

Monsieur the Governor had given orders to fire several Cannon shots at the Elevation, when our brother the sacristan should give the Signal; but he forgot it, and thus there was no salute. The people received Communion at the end of high mass; after which a low mass was said.

There were four candles in the Church in small iron candlesticks in the form of a Bracket, and that is enough. There were, besides, two great kettles full of fire, furnished by the warehouse in order to warm the chapel; they were kindled beforehand, on the bridge. Direction had been given to remove them after mass, but, that having been neglected,

---

*The piece of the consecrated bread which is sent to the person who is to furnish the bread on the Sunday Morning following.

the fire caught in the night on the floor which was under one of the kettles, in which there were not enough ashes at the bottom. But fortunately, *dirigente Domino,* the fire did not appear till toward 5 o'clock in the morning, above our hall or refectory, and kitchen, in which was pierre gontier, our Cook,—who, perceiving this, immediately went up, and, without other noise, put out the fire.

JESUIT RELATIONS

Father Jean Enjalran Writes from St. Ignace, 1679

All our savages, but especially the hurons, profess to have a special esteem for the all-endearing mystery of the birth of our lord Jesus Christ. I have seen some notable proofs of this given by these latter; they themselves entreated the father, long before the feast-day, to make arrangements so as to celebrate it in the most solemn manner possible. They sent their children to seek for what could be used in constructing a grotto, in which they were to make a representation of the mystery; and I took pleasure in hearing a little girl who, having brought with much care a beautiful sort of grass, said that she had done it in the thought and hope that the little infant Jesus might be Laid upon that grass. Our good Christians made some more serious preparations, For they all confessed; and those to whom permission was given to receive Communion, did so very devoutly, at the midnight mass. The grotto, which was well fitted to inspire devotion, was Incessantly visited; and it rendered a very pleasing although rather protracted Service,—to draw from them the expression of their feelings as they themselves express them, when addressing the divine child. As a Climax to their devotion, they asked that the infant Jesus should do them the favour of visiting them, by being carried through their village. But, as they thought that they had rendered themselves Unworthy of this by some things that had taken place, they held grand Councils and took great precautions to obtain this favour from their missionary. The Matter was conceded to them, and carried out on the Day of the epiphany in a manner that seems to me worthy of being recorded. For my part, I was much touched by it.

They desired, then, in execution of their design, to imitate what in other ages had been done by the three great stranger Captains, who came to confess and adore Jesus Christ in the Manger, and afterward went to preach him in their own country. All the hurons, Christians and non-Christians, divided themselves into three companies, according to the different nations that constitute their village; and, after choosing their Chiefs, one for each nation, they furnished them with porcelain, of which they were to make an offering to the infant Jesus. Every one adorned himself as handsomely as he could. The three Captains had each a scepter in his hand, to which was fastened the offering, and wore a gaudy head-dress in guise of a crown. Each company took up a different position. The signal for marching having been given them at the sound of the trumpet, they heeded the sound as that of a voice Inviting them to go to see and adore an infant God new-born. Just as the 1st company took up their march,—conducted by a star fastened to a large standard of the Colour of Sky-blue, and having at the *rear* (head) their Captain, before whom was carried his banner,—The 2nd company, seeing the first marching, demanded of them (aloud) the object of their journey; and on learning it, they Joined themselves to them, having in like manner their chief at their head with his banner. The 3rd company, more advanced on the road, did as the second; and, one after another, they continued their march, and entered our Church, the star remaining at the entrance. The 3 chiefs, having first prostrated themselves, and laid their Crowns and sceptres at the feet of the infant Jesus in the Cradle, offered their Congratulations and presents to their saviour. As they did so, they made a public protestation of the submission and obedience that they desired to render him; solicited faith for those who possessed it not, and protection for all their nation and for all that land; and, in conclusion, entreated him to approve that they should bring him into their village, of which they desired he should be the master. I was engaged in carrying the little statue of the divine infant, which inspired great devotion; I took it from the grotto, and from its cradle, and carried it on a fine linen cloth. Every one seemed touched, and Pressed forward in the crowd, to get a nearer view of the holy Child. Our hurons left the church in the same order in which they had come. I came after them, carrying the little statue, preceded by two frenchmen bearing a large standard, on which was represented the infant Jesus with his holy mother. All the algonquins—and especially the christians, who had been invited to assist in the pious function—followed, and accompanied the infant Jesus. They marched, then, in that order toward the village, Chanting the litanies of the virgin, and went into a Cabin of our hurons, where they had prepared for Jesus a lodging, as appropriate as they could make it. There they offered thanksgivings and prayers, in accordance with their devotion; and the divine child was conducted back to the church and replaced in the grotto. The Christian algonquins were afterward invited by the Christian hurons to a feast, at which they exhorted each other to obey Jesus Christ, who was the true master of the world. After this feast, at which, according to their Custom, the hurons did not eat, another and a special one was prepared for all the Christian and non-Christian hurons, spread by the officers in turn. This feast was preceded by a dance, as is their custom, whose sole object was that they might Rejoice together at the favour that they had received in the Visit which the new-born child had paid to their village. This dance is performed by the women only, as I said,—ranging themselves in two parallel lines at the two Sides of a Cabin, having in their hands a kind of Castanet. Those who are officers commence the Song and dance; they have some words to which they apply one of their airs, and these form the refrain of their Song which every one is to repeat to the same air. While the One who has Begun Goes on with her Song agreeably to the words which have served her for a refrain,—very often, however, varying the air,—she Runs and bustles about between these two ranks in a singular manner. In this there is nothing, as formerly, to violate decency, especially on occasions in which they claim to honour God. Meanwhile the others—repeating at certain intervals the words which form the refrain, and which explain the intention of the one who is dancing—sound their Castanets, and move sometimes one foot, sometimes the other, to Certain measures without leaving their places. When some word which pleases them occurs in the Song they redouble the noise of their castanets, and their cries of Joy. Each does, in her turn, the same as the first; and it is required of each that she have a special refrain and Song. The refrains and Songs of that day were but praises and thanksgivings—addressed sometimes to the holy child, sometimes to his holy mother, and, again, to the missionaries who had procured them such a benefit. The non-Christian women had, of course, to do as the Christians, to whose happiness they aspired; and many, assuredly, form the purpose, on these occasions, to embrace Christianity. After the dance and feast, all the Christians came to the church to receive the benediction of the blessed sacrament.

JESUIT RELATIONS

Christmas in the Fur Trade

★ ★ ★ ★ ★ ★ ★ ★ ★ ★ ★ ★ ★ ★ ★ ★ ★ ★ ★ ★

Christmastime down the years has been celebrated by the men of the Hudson's Bay Company in many far, strange corners of the continent. It has found some ensconced in the cheery atmosphere of a comfortable fort, some at a lonely outpost in the wilderness, some still travelling on the snowy trail. But few have failed to mark the joyous season in one way or another. To the Scotsman, and the French-Canadian of course, Christmas Day was not as important as New Years. Fort Chipewyan, for example, in 1823 ignored the former but celebrated the latter.

One of these festive occasions was curious, in that the merrymakers drank the health of a queen nearly five months dead. Michael Grimington, in the journal of Albany Factory, James Bay, wrote on Christmas Day 1714: 'Wee keep Christmast Day wth. Drinking the Queens Health and the Compies.' Anne had certainly been on the throne when the Company's ship sailed from London in the spring, bearing Captain James Knight with her royal commission to take over the Bay forts from the French. But she had died on August 1st, and George I reigned in her stead.

Ten years later, at the same post, R. Staunton wrote in his journal: 'This beinge Christmas daye the People observed the same as usual in this remote part of the worlde, but not with the pleasure and sattisfactione as if the Companyes ship and cargoe had gone safe home, wch. makes us all feare the worse, not only at this time but all the yeare.' He was referring to the ship Mary, which had been sunk after leaving Albany that fall, with all her rich cargo of furs.

At Moose Factory, the form of celebration varied with the religious scruples of the master. James Duffield, who seems to have been a jolly soul, wrote on Christmas Day 1741: 'At noon gave each Mess a bottle of Wine & in the evening a gallon pot of Strong beer to Celebrate the happy time—At 8 saw them all to bed, not forgetting the Conflagration 6 years past.' (This refers to the fire on December 26, 1735, when the fort was destroyed by a fire that started in the 'cook room'.) In 1747, however, Christmas at Moose Factory could hardly have been described as merry. 'Spent the Day in Religious Exercise,' wrote dour John Potts, 'and to prevent hard Drinking I did Read over to them one of the Little Books Your Honrs. was pleased to Send us Last Year, wch. is a Disswasive from the Sin of Drunkenness. I gave them a Little Liqur. in the Evening and at Eight O Clock Ordered all hands to bed and the Lights out.'

Jollity was the order of the day at Albany in 1749: 'Having three Fidlers in the Factory,' wrote the master, 'viz. Geo. Millar, Willm. Murray & James Short, our People celebrated the Evening with Dancing & Singing, and were all very merry: keept a carefull Look out in case of Fire.' . . .

Pathetic by comparison is Thomas Stagner's entry in the journal for 1789 of Manchester House, on the North Saskatchewan. 'This being Christmas Morning, our small Stock of Flour, afforded us, a Cake to eat, with a little Tea & Chocolate, (which we all appearently enjoyed very much) no one can know what it is to want Bread, but those who experience it, (which we here, daily do, in this Wild Country; particular Holidays only excepted).'

New Year's Day 1797, at Brandon House, on the prairies, was a very festive occasion, marked by fraternization with the Company's rivals. James Sutherland recorded that: 'In the morning the Canadians (Nor'westers) make the House and yard Ring with salluting, the House then filld with them when they all got a dram each, after they were gone the House filld a second time with Ladys the wives of the Canadians with the Complimentary Kiss of the new year according to their Custom and drest in their wedding garments, and had a dram to give each of them also.'

At Osnaburgh House two years later there was more fraternization with the Nor'westers. 'I had the honour of my Neighbours company to dinner,' wrote John McKay on Christmas Day. And he added with a touch of dry Scots humour, 'Your Honours has the honour of bearing the expences.'

Towards the close of the struggle between the two great companies, however, there was no such comradeship evident. George Simpson wrote on Christmas Day from Lake Athabaska, near the North-West Company Fort Chipewyan: 'This being Xmas day the people had a dram in the morning and were allowed to make holyday. The Gentlemen sat down to the most sumptuous Dinner that Fort Wedderburn could afford, true English fare, Roast Beef and plum pudding and afterwards a temperate Kettle of Punch. McGillivray paid his Friends at the Watch house a visit for about half an hour; they seem to muster unusually strong and I have directed a guard to be kept to night. The weather bitterly cold.'

In 1847, Paul Kane the artist whose paintings of the Canadian west are still highly prized, spent Christmas Day at Fort Edmonton, the headquarters of the Saskatchewan District. He writes:

'On Christmas-day the flag was hoisted, and all appeared in their best and gaudiest style, to do honour to the holiday . . . About two o'clock we sat down to dinner. Our party consisted of Mr. Harriett, the chief, and three clerks, Mr. Thebo (Thibault?), the Roman Catholic missionary from Manitou Lake about thirty miles off, Mr. Rundell (Rundle), the Wesleyan missionary, who resided within the pickets, and myself . . .

'The dining-hall in which we assembled was the largest room in the fort, probably about fifty by twenty-five feet, well warmed by large fires, which are scarcely ever allowed to go out. The walls and ceilings are boarded, as plastering is not used, there being no limestone within reach; but these boards are painted in a style of the most startling barbaric gaudiness, and the ceiling filled with centrepieces of fantastic gilt scrolls, making altogether a saloon which no white man would enter for the first time without a start, and which the Indians always looked upon with awe and wonder.

'The room was intended as a reception room for the wild chiefs who visited the fort; and the artist who designed the decorations was no doubt directed to "astonish the natives". If such were his instructions, he deserves the highest praise for having faithfully complied with them . . . No table-cloth shed its snowy whiteness over the board; no silver candelabra or gaudy china interfered with its simple magnificence. The bright tin plates and dishes reflected jolly faces, and burnished gold can give no truer zest to a feast.

'At the head, before Mr. Harriett, was a large dish of boiled buffalo hump; at the foot smoked a boiled buffalo calf. Start not, gentle reader, the calf is very small, and is taken from the cow by the Caesarean operation long before it attains its full growth. This, boiled whole, is one of the most esteemed dishes amongst the epicures of the interior. My pleasing duty was to help a dish of mouffle, or dried moose nose; the gentleman on my left distributed the white fish, delicately browned in buffalo marrow. The priest helped the buffalo tongue, whilst Mr. Rundell cut up the beavers' tails. Nor was the other gentleman left unemployed, as all his spare time was occupied in dissecting a roast wild goose. The centre of the table was graced with piles of potatoes, turnips, and bread conveniently placed, so that each could help himself without interrupting the labours of his companions. Such was our jolly Christmas dinner at Edmonton; and long will it remain in my memory, although no pies, or puddings, or blanc manges, shed their fragrance over the scene.

'In the evening the hall was prepared for the dance to which Mr. Harriett had invited all the inmates of the fort, and was early filled by the gaily dressed guests. Indians, whose chief ornament consisted in the paint on their faces, voyageurs with bright sashes and neatly ornamented moccasins, half-breeds glittering in every ornament they could lay their hands on; whether civilised or savage, all were laughing, and jabbering in as many different languages as there were styles of dress. English, however, was little used, as none could speak it but those who sat at the dinner-table. The dancing was most picturesque, and almost all joined in it . . .

'After enjoying ourselves with such boisterous vigour for several hours, we all gladly retired to rest about twelve o'clock, the guests separating in great good humour, not only with themselves but with their entertainers.'

THE BEAVER

Travelling to the Northern Ocean, 1770

On the nineteenth, we pursued our course in the North West quarter; and, after leaving the above-mentioned creek, traversed nothing but entire barren ground, with empty bellies, till the twenty-seventh; for though we arrived at some woods on the twenty-sixth, and saw a few deer, four of which the Indians killed, they were at so great a distance from the place on which we lay, that it was the twenty-seventh before the meat was brought to the tents. Here the Indians proposed to continue one day, under pretence of repairing their sledges and snow shoes; but from the little attention they paid to those repairs, I was led to think that the want of food was the chief thing that detained them, as they never ceased eating the whole day. Indeed for many days before we had been in great want, and for the last three days had not tasted a morsel of any thing, except a pipe of tobacco and a drink of snow water; and as we walked daily from morning till night and were all heavy laden, our strength began to fail. I must confess that I never spent so dull a Christmas; and when I recollected the merry season which was then passing, and reflected on the immense quantities, and great variety of delicacies which were then expending in every part of Christendom, and that with a profusion bordering on waste, I could not refrain from wishing myself again in Europe, if it had been only to have had an opportunity of alleviating the extreme hunger which I suffered with the refuse of any table of any one of my acquaintance. My Indians, however, still kept in good spirits; and as we were then across all the barren ground, and saw a few fresh tracks of deer, they began to think that the worst of the road was over for that winter, and flattered me with the expectation of soon meeting with deer and other game in greater plenty than we had done since our departure from the Fort.

SAMUEL HEARNE

Pioneer Celebrations

It was the year after the memorable rebellion in Canada: my brother-in-law had been appointed to a company in the Provincial Battalion in Toronto; my sister who had remained behind with her infant family was alone, and we were anxious that she should spend this day with us, and that it might look more like an English Christmas Day, I despatched Martin, the boy, and old Malachi, the hired man, to bring a sleigh load of evergreens, from the swamp to dress the house with, but when all our green garlands were put up, we missed the bright varnished holly and its gay joy-inspiring red berries, and my English maid Hannah, who was greatly interested in all our decorations, remembered that there were highbush cranberries, at the lake shore, and winter greens in the swamp, but these last were deep beneath a covering of two or three feet of snow. With the red transparent berries of the cranberry we were obliged therefore to content ourselves . . .

Then we sent off the ox sleigh for my sister, and her little ones, for be it known, to you, dear reader, that our settlement in those days was almost the Ultima Thule of civilization, and our roads were no roads, only wide openings chopped through the heart of the forest along which no better vehicle than an ox sleigh could make any progress without the continual chance of an overturn. We bush-settlers were brave folks then, and thankfully enjoyed every pleasure we could meet with, even though we had to seek it through means so humble as a ride in a rude vehicle like an ox sleigh, through the wild woods, with the snow above, and the snow below . . .

A glorious goose fattened on the rice bed in our lake, was killed for the occasion: turkeys were only to be met with on old cleared farms in those days, and beef was rarely seen in the back woods—excepting when some old ox . . . was slaughtered to save it from dying a natural death. Remember this was sixteen years ago, and great changes have taken place since that time in the condition of all ranks of people in the Province; now there are luxuries, where before necessities were scarce. However there was no lack of Christmas cheer in the shape of a large plum pudding to which our little ones did ample justice. A merry day it was to them, for our boy Martin had made them a little sledge, and there was a famous snow drift against the garden fence, which was hard packed and frozen smooth and glare—up and down this frozen heap did James and Katie with their playmates glide and roll. It was a Christmas treat to watch those joyous faces, buoyant with mirth, and brightened by the keen air, through the frosty panes . . .

CATHERINE PARR TRAILL

In Newfoundland, 1842

Two special seasons are devoted in the large towns to merry meetings—
Christmas and the New Year. At St. John's, on St. Stephen's day, little
boys go about from door to door, with a green bush from the spruce
trees, decorated with ribands and paper, (in which, if they can get one,
is a little bird, to represent the wren,) and repeat the following verse, or
something of the same kind:—

> 'The wren, the wren, the king of all birds,
> Was caught on St. Stephen's day in the firs,
> Although he is little, his honour is great;
> So rise up, kind madame, and give us a treat.
> Up with the kettle, and down with the pan;
> A penny, or twopence, to bury the wren.*
> Your pocket full of money, and your cellar full of beer,
> I wish you all a merry Christmas, and a happy new year.'

This ancient custom is, of course, derived from home, as well as that
of the mummers, who assemble on New Year's day; the former from
Ireland probably, the latter from the West of England.

There was, and still is, a sort of saturnalia amongst the lower classes,
in St. John's particularly, and which lasts three days, commencing at
Christmas, with boys only.

The mummers prepare, before the New Year, dresses of all possible
shapes and hues, most of which are something like those of harlequin
and the clown in pantomimes, but the general colour is white, with
sundry bedaubments of tinsel and paint. A huge paper cocked hat is one
favourite headpiece, and every one, among the gentlemen, excepting
the captain or leader, and his two or three assistants, is masked. The
ladies are represented by young fishermen, who are painted, but not
masked. Some of the masks are very grotesque, and the fools or clowns
are furnished with thongs and bladders, with which they belabour the

*Pronounced here always wran

exterior mob. Much ingenuity is observable in the style of the cocked hats, which are surmounted with all sorts of things, feathers in profusion, paper models of ships, etc.

They go to the Government House first, and then round to the inhabitants; and it has been customary to make the captain a present of money for a ball, which is given at the end of the carnival, if it may be so styled.

They perform, at those houses which admit them, a sort of play, in which the unmasked characters only take a part, and which is very long and tiresome after once hearing. It is a dialogue between the captain and a sailor, and commences with Alexander the Great, and continues down to Nelson and Wellington. They are both armed with swords, and a mock fight goes on all the while, till one is supposed to be slain, when the doctor is called in to bring him to life again.

I cannot recollect the doggrel used, but as it is a relic of the days of the Abbot of Unreason and the Lord of Misrule, it is interesting and harmless. I never remember to have seen anything in England (though, to be sure, I have not been much in my native country since my boyhood), resembling it, excepting the now very rare morris-dancers, whom I once saw in perfection near Aylesbury in Buckinghamshire, when a boy, and who almost exactly resembled those described as depicted on painted glass, in an old English mansion, in the notes to Johnson and Steeven's Shakspeare.

SIR RICHARD HENRY BONNYCASTLE

Louis Riel's Joke

★ ★

From August to December 6, 1869, I was working on a Government highway between St. Boniface and the Northwest Angle, Manitoba. The foreman was Mr. Snow. Early in the morning of December 6 a half-breed carrier, sent by Governor William McDougall, advised us to report for duty at Fort Garry as soon as possible.

So six men and myself immediately set out. We made the journey in one and one-half days. The weather was bitterly cold and snowy, and I had the misfortune to freeze my big toes.

While we were crossing the Red River, about seven p.m., Louis Riel's soldiers stopped us with the command, '*Arrêtez*—You are under arrest'.

We were taken to the Schultz's residence, which had been captured by the rebels. We had the pleasure of occupying, that night, Mrs. Schultz's bedroom. Next morning we were marched to Fort Garry as prisoners. Here we were held until January 16, 1870.

At the time Fort Garry was the headquarters of the Hudson's Bay trading post. No free traders were permitted within one mile.

Our food in Fort Garry consisted of dry pemmican and water, three times a day.

Christmas Day dawned cold and gloomy. We did not lack company, as there were forty-five of us in a very small room.

After a breakfast of pemmican we sang hymns, chatted about home folks, and talked of our possible doom. As dinner time drew near, we thought of the fat turkeys and puddings that would be gracing some tables in the East. We expected the usual fare, but suddenly one of Riel's men brought before us a steaming boiler of hot coffee, and sugar and milk, along with a clothesbasket brimming with delicious buttered buns. This meal was kindly prepared by three ladies—Mrs. George Young, Mrs. Crowson, and Mrs. Charles Major. They had received permission from Riel to make our Christmas more cheerful.

I will never forget that hot coffee, it was so refreshing and stimulating. The buns seemed just to hit the right spot. This tasty meal gave us fresh courage, as it let us know that someone was thinking of us and was interested in our case.

All afternoon we carried buckets of water from the Red River to the fort. For what good reason did not appear, but I think to this day that the rebels made us carry it through sheer ugliness, as Riel emptied each bucket of water on the ground as it came.

However, that night, as we went to bed on the usual damp floor, we dreamed of the delicious Christmas dinner we had enjoyed in Fort Garry, prisoners of Louis Riel.

R. P. OTTEWELL

Rideau Hall, 1872

Christmas Day.—Thermometer 20° below zero. Proprieties out of the question—must go to church in sealskin turbans, and must undress when we get there, as we sit near the stove; so that when we leave, the amount of things to be put on is frightful. There are my cloak, and my cloud, fur gauntlets, and woolen cuffs; there are Archie's coat, and his cloud, and turban, and gloves. Then Fred and D. have to be clothed; happily, every one in the church is equally busy muffling up. D., you will be surprised to hear, wears absolutely less than he used to do in May at home, and scarcely seems to feel the cold at all. Fred, too, bears it well, with the exception of his ears, about which he is decidedly nervous. He is always feeling them and inquiring from passers-by whether they are frozen. The children play in the snow as if it were hay, and enjoy themselves immensely. Their nurse, Mrs. Hall, dislikes the wrapping up, but has been consoled by a present of a pair of skates. Their governess is learning too; she won't wrap up, and I really fear some accident for her: nothing but a frostbite will make her careful.

We have arranged a Christmas tree, and this evening all the children of the family assembled for it. They came at five, and the nine of them, with their governesses and nurses, were ushered into the room with great ceremony. Hermie rushed at a doll. 'There is my doll,' and kissed it most fervently. Of course they all got various presents, and the big ones dined with us, and afterward played blind man's buff, snapdragon, etc., etc.

The pictures have arrived, and are a great improvement to the house. In my room I have drawings of Killyleagh and Clandeboye, and there are a few oil-portraits in the dining-room, which make it look home-like. We shall be quite sorry to go away next week, to undertake a long journey in the snow, and to be a month in hotels.

THE MARCHIONESS OF DUFFERIN AND AVA

First Days in Manitoba

Christmas was a jolly time that year. We had spruce boughs, brought from the Sandhills, across the doors and windows, and streamers of red tissue paper and red and green balls, made from tissue paper cut in circles, folded and sewed together. Mrs. Lundy had showed Hannah how to make these, when Hannah had stayed with her in the summer holidays. Mr. and Mrs. Lundy had a store about a mile east of Millford.

I remember particularly the apple-jelly tarts that we had at Christmas and how delicious they were. The apple-jelly was bright red in color, for snow apples were now sold in Mr. Lundy's store and mother had used only the parings and cores for the jelly, and the other part was made into apple sauce . . .

Christmas Day has always been flavored to me with the pound cake and apple-jelly tarts of those first days in Manitoba.

The front-room always got a new coat of white-wash on the log walls at Christmas, and everything was scoured as white as sand or soap could make it. The hand-knit lace curtains, brought from Ontario, were washed and starched and stretched on home-made frames, so they would hang straight and reach the floor. Short curtains were considered slightly indecent. The two long widths of rag carpet in bright stripes with orange warp were brought out, laid on the white floor, with the good mats, one hooked and one braided. The home-made lounge had a covering of dark maroon canton flannel and was well supplied with patch work cushions, crazy pattern of silks and satins and two log cabins, one made of 'stuff pieces', the other one of prints. There were two book-cases made with spools, painted black, and set with shelves and a 'what-not' of five shelves, on which stood china ornaments, a shell box, with a green plush pin-cushion on the top, apples filled with cloves, and cups and saucers, (honourably retired from active service because of cracks, or missing handles, but with these defects tactfully concealed in the way they were placed), coloured glass mugs, and on the top, a bouquet of prairie grasses, set in a frosted glass vase, a lace pattern on deep blue. I remember it well, for I broke it years later, when bouncing a ball, on the floor.

When the weather got cold, the kitchen stove had to be brought into the big room, and it was a family grief when this change had to be made. If the weather did not come down too hard, the stove was kept out until after Christmas. Later when the storm doors and windows were added, and a bigger heater bought, a fine big barrel of a stove, with a row of mica windows around its middle, through which the coals glowed with all the colours of a sunset, the kitchen stove remained in the kitchen all winter.

But even when the kitchen stove was in the middle of the big room, there was a cheerful roominess about it. The woodbox papered with pictures of the Ice Palace, in Montreal, (*Family Herald Supplement*) when covered with two boards over which a quilt was spread made a nice warm seat and when we got the hanging lamp from Brandon, with a pale pink shade, on which a brown deer poised for a leap across a chasm, through which a green stream dashed in foam on the rocks, the effect was magical and in the pink light the white-washed walls were softened into alabaster.

We had two new pictures now, enlarged photographs of father and mother in heavy oak frames with a gilt edge, done by a travelling artist, who drove a team of mules and carried a few lines of tinware. Every family in the neighborhood had taken advantage of his easy plan to secure a lasting work of art. You paid only for the frame and received the picture entirely free though this offer might be withdrawn any minute for he was doing this merely to get his work known. He said there was no nicer way to give one's parents a pleasant surprise, and the pictures would be delivered in time for Christmas. When they came, we all had a surprise. We had thought that the seven dollars and thirty-five cents paid for both frames but we were wrong. Each one cost that amount and even at that the artist was losing money. The pictures were accepted and hung on the log walls, and in the declivities behind them were kept tissue paper patterns, newspaper clippings, and other semi-precious documents, thus relieving the congestion in the real archives, lodged in the lower regions of the clock, where notes, grain-tickets, tax receipts were kept.

NELLIE McCLUNG

Reverie

When it was midnight, I walked out, and strolled in the woods . . . I was suddenly roused from a delicious reverie by observing a dark object moving slowly and cautiously among the trees. At first I fancied it was a bear but a nearer inspection discovered an Indian on all fours. For a moment I felt unwilling to throw myself in his way lest he should be meditating some sinister design against me; however on his waving his hand and putting his finger on his lips, I approached him, and notwithstanding his injunction to silence, inquired what he did there. 'Me watch to see the deer kneel,' replied he. 'This is Christmas night, and all the deer fall upon their knees to the Great Spirit, and look up.' The solemnity of the scene and the grandeur of the idea alike contributed to fill me with awe.

JOHN HOWISON

*From
Sea to Sea*

Christmas Customs

My thoughts today fly far from Toronto. They come to earth at the main intersection of the little town of Canora, Saskatchewan. Santa Claus knows all about Canora—he knows it is a prairie town close to the border of Manitoba and north from Regina. Santa Claus has two X's after his Christmas list for Canora; he makes two trips to Canora. Whether he comes by reindeer, horse or tractor, Santa carries a light load when he visits Canora on the eve of December 25th. In fact, he passes right over many homes. And Santa knows that the Christmas tree at the main intersection, gay with lights and drooping with decoration will be glowing long after most Christmas trees have been taken down. Two weeks from now that Christmas tree will be more magic than ever. Even as late as January seventh, many Canadians who live in and near Canora will honour their Christmas tree, for on that day Ukranian Canadians and other members of the Greek Orthodox Church mark the birth of the infant Jesus. Yes, Christ was born on Christmas Day. But, when is Christmas Day? Depends on who you are. 'CHRISTMAS—WHICH—WHOSE?'

But, let's look around. Let's break down the customs of Christmas and we'll see how they vary even within our own country. Let's take the largest ethnic group in Canada—the French-speaking Canadians. There are close to five million of them. To many of them, Christmas is a sacred day. In the smaller communities it starts with Mass at midnight and then a feast in the middle of the night. They call this *reveillon*. They eat frozen puddings, *ragoûts*, stews and lovely old French dishes. Christmas is not a gay lighthearted day with Jean Baptiste. The day for good cheer and merry-making and whoop-la in Montreal and Quebec City is at New Year's—never Christmas.

In this country of many backgrounds, some Canadians believe that the Epiphany—January 6, is the Holy Day—the glorious day when the little child of Bethlehem was shown to the wise men—when He was revealed to the Gentiles is the most important festival—and that comes twelve days after our celebration of Christ's birth. So, we have December 25, January 6, January 7—all Holy Days.

Santa Claus does not always come down the chimney; and he does not always use reindeer. This idea of the reindeer galloping over the roof tops only started about a century ago when Dr. Clement Clarke Moore wrote his poem: ' 'Twas the Night before Christmas.' Ever since eight reindeer have been galloping over the homes. The Dutch have never adopted the idea of reindeer. They stick to the old idea of the eight-footed horse Sleipner. So do the Scandinavians—and they should know something about this yuletide season because we borrowed the name from them. The Scandinavian word JUL referring to the pagan feast has been blended into the word yuletide and yule log.

And, speaking of the Dutch and their eight-footed horse Sleipner, if you went down to the fruit farms of Beamsville, Ontario, up around the famous Holland Marshes of Ontario, into the Dutch settlements of Northern New Brunswick and out in the tulip and daffodil rows of the Fraser Valley, you would find many Canadians of Dutch origin who start Christmas on December the sixth. December sixth is St. Nicholas Eve, when children put out their shoes and fill them with grain for Sleipner the horse. If they have been good little children, Sleipner leaves them toys and presents, but if they have been bad, they awake to find switches.

Not only the Canadians of Dutch ancestry observe St. Nicholas Day; so do the Mennonites. Their Christmas lasts four weeks—from December 6 to January 6. On St. Nicholas Eve, St. Nick himself, in the household, appears with a whip in hand, and cracking it ominously, inquires about the children's behavior during the year. When St. Nick comes, he tosses nuts and wrapped candies all over the floor. And again on Christmas Eve the Mennonites have a special custom—each one takes a plate and they leave their plates with names attached overnight on the table. On Christmas morning, they are filled with fruit. The Mennonites have many Church services surrounding Christmas. On the Epiphany they burn three-armed candles in honor of the Three Wise Men, and on that night every girl is excited, for if she looks in her mirror at midnight, and she is quite alone, she will see the face of the man she is going to marry.

And today, on my Christmas, and with my British-American background I ate turkey, nuts and Christmas pudding. I did, yes, but many, many Canadians ate no meat at all. Many of our Ukranian people observe a six weeks' fast in which they eat no meat preceding their Christmas on January 7. On Christmas Eve many fast all day until the stars peep out at night, then the family gathers about the dinner table reverently. On the table, a little hay is scattered to remind them of the manger in far-off Bethlehem. A sheaf of wheat is stood in the corner of the room and beneath the table, in which nuts are hidden. After dinner the children will scramble and play in the straw seeking the nuts. On the day after Christmas, all the straw is carried outside to the gate of the homestead and burnt. And at many Ukranian tables after a solemn prayer by the father, he takes a spoonful of *koot'yah*, boiled wheat and honey and tosses it in the air. The family catch it with delight, for each grain they catch signifies a hive of bees which they will find in the coming year. *Koot'yah* is the first of twelve courses served—courses to signify the twelve apostles. And they eat borsch, jellied stuffed fish, stuffed cabbage, figs, and honey cake and so on—a long exotic list, and rarely is turkey served. This feast lasts for hours.

When I was in The Pas, Manitoba, Bob Taylor, editor of the paper there, told me about how the Indian children from the North were begging their school teacher to bring them Santa Claus with cows and horses. They had seen plenty of deer and caribou, but they had never seen a horse and that would be a real treat to them. Christmas and its customs depends on where you live, who you are, and what you believe or do.

Religion, background and geography, each one has fashioned customs of its own. The Indians of Canada who learned of Christmas from the White Man have added legends of their own. They believe that at midnight on Christmas Eve all the deer in the forest kneel with their heads bowed low—pointing to the town of Bethlehem, where the great Manitou sent them their Saviour.

Here in Canada we have the rich wealth of custom to cherish—custom brought from all the lands of the earth, seasoned with our own versions and blended like the fruits of a plum pudding into a satisfying whole. We have the Christ Tree of Bavaria, the Yule Log of Scandinavia, the watchful St. Nicholas of Holland and England's mistletoe.

And then we have a quarter of a million Canadians—good, fine

Canadians to whom Christmas is just another day of the week—the Jews, Buddhists and Confucians. Some 170,000 Jewish Canadians do not have Christmas. They have an inspiring religious festival of their own which is called Chanuchak (Han You Kah)—the feast of dedication—which takes place shortly before Christmas and lasts eight days. It is at this festival that the orthodox Jews exchange gifts and crowd their synagogues. And the same for the Chinese. They do not recognize Christmas in their religions—nor do many Canadians whose racial roots are traced to the Orient. The big time for the Chinese Canadians is at their New Year many, many weeks from now.

And so we see there is no uniformity about Christmas in such a tremendous country as Canada. Christmas is not the Santa Claus bag of gifts, the merchandising schemes, the advertising; to each one of us it is the custom cherished. Some eat turkey, others eat pork, roast duck or fish. Some eat plum pudding, others eat rice, porridge with one hidden almond, and the Scandinavian Canadian who finds the almond will have his wish come true. Some exchange gifts, others don't. The French-speaking Canadian says: 'Joyeux Noel' when Canadians say Merry Christmas—and scores of thousands of Ukranian Canadians use neither word: When they meet they say 'Christ is born' and the person replies 'Praised be the Lord.' Christmas to some Canadians is a feast, to others a fast. Christmas in Newfoundland comes and goes six and one-half hours before the Yukon people celebrate. And so at this season of Good Will, perhaps this is an opportunity to see how diversified and big Canada really is.

JOHN FISHER

How Santa Claus Came to Cape St. Anthony

▲ ▲

A universal robe of white had long covered our country-side, hiding every vestige of our rocky soil, and every trace of the great summer fishery. The mail steamer had paid its last visit for six months; and thus the last link with civilization was broken. Even the loitering sea-ducks and lesser auks had left us. The iron grip of winter lay on sea and shore.

At its best, the land here scarcely suggests the word *country* to a southerner—scarcely even the word *moors*. For the rock is everywhere close to the surface, and mosses and lichens are its chief products. The larger part of the country we call *barrens*. Few of the houses deserve even to be called cottages, for all are of light, rough wood. Most are of only one story, and contain but two rooms. The word *huts* would convey a more accurate idea of these humble abodes. The settlements themselves are small and scattered, and at this time the empty tilts of the summer fishermen give a still more desolate aspect to these lonely habitations.

Early in December we had been dumped from the little mail steamer on the harbor ice about half a mile from shore, and hauled up to the little Mission hospital, where we were to make our headquarters for the winter. The name of our harbor was St. Anthony. Christmas was close upon us. The prospect of enjoying the conventional pleasures of the season was not bright. Not unnaturally our thoughts went over the sea to the family gathering at home, at which our places would be vacant. We should miss the holly and mistletoe, the roast beef and plum-pudding, the inevitable crackers, and the giving and receiving of presents, which had always seemed essential to a full enjoyment of the Christmas holiday.

We soon found that few of the children here had ever possessed a toy; and that there was scarcely a single girl that owned a doll. Now and again one would see, nailed high up on the wall, well out of reach of the children, a flimsy, cheaply painted doll; and the mother would explain that her 'Pa had got un from a trader, sir, for thirty cents. No, us don't allow Nellie to have it, 'feared lest she might spoil un'—a fear I found to be only too well grounded when I came to examine its anatomy more closely.

Christmas trees in plenty grew near the hospital; and we could easily arrange for a 'Father Christmas'. The only question was, whether our stock of toys would justify us in inviting so many children as would want to come. It is easy to satisfy children like these, however, and so we announced that we expected Santa Claus on a certain day. There was great talk about the affair. Whispers reached us that Aunt Mary thought her Joe weren't too big to come; sure, he'd be only sixteen. May White was only going eighteen, and she would so like to come. Old Daddy Gilliam would like to sit in a corner. He'd never seen a Christmas tree, and he was nigh on eighty. We were obliged to yield, and with guilty consciences expected twice as many as the room would hold. All through the day before the event the Sister was busy making buns; and it was even whispered that a barrel of apples had been carried over to the 'room'.

In the evening a sick call carried me north to a tiny place on the Straits of Belle Isle, where a woman lay in great pain, and by all accounts dying. The dogs were in great form, and travelling was fair enough till we came to a great arm of the sea, which lay right in our path, and was only recently caught over with young ice. To reach the other shore we had to make a wide detour, bumping our way along the rough edge of the old standing ice. Even here the salt water came up through the snow, and the dogs sank to their shoulders in a cold mush that made each mile into half a dozen. We began to think that our chance of getting back in time on the morrow was small indeed. We were also wondering that it seemed to be a real disappointment to ourselves that we should miss the humble attempt at Christmas keeping.

One thing went a long way toward reconciling us to the disappointment. The case we had come to see proved to be one in which skilled help was of real service. So we were a contented company round the log fire in the little hut, as we sat listening to stories from one and another of the neighbors, who, according to custom, had dropped in to see the stranger. Before long my sleeping bag was loudly calling to me after the exercise of the day. 'We must be off by dawn, Uncle Phil, for there's no counting on these short days, and we have promised to see that Santa Claus is in time for the Christmas tree to-morrow night at St. Anthony.' Soon, stretched out on the floor, we slept as soundly as in a feather bed.

Only a few minutes seemed to have passed when, ' 'Twill be dawning shortly, Doctor,' in the familiar tones of my driver's voice, came filtering into my bag. 'Right you are, Rube; put the kettle on and call the dogs; I will be ready in a couple of shakes.'

Oh, what a glorious morning! An absolute stillness, and the air as sweet as sugar. Everywhere a mantle of perfect white below, a fathomless depth of cloudless blue overhead—and the first radiance of the coming day blending one into the other with a rich, transparent red. The bracing cold made one feel twenty years younger. We found it a hard job to tackle up the dogs, they were so mad to be off. As we topped the first hill the great bay that had caused us so much trouble lay below us, and my driver gave a joyous shout.' Hurrah, Doctor! there's a lead for us.' Far out on the ice he had spied a black speck moving toward the opposite shore. A *komatik* had ventured over the young ice, and to follow it would mean a saving of five miles to us.

We had made a good landing and scaled the opposite hill, and were galloping over the high barrens, when the dogs began to give tongue, loudly announcing that a team was coming from the opposite direction. As we drew near, a muffled figure jumped off, and hauling his dogs to one side, shouted the customary, 'What cheer?'

Then a surprised, 'The Doctor, as I live! You're the very man I'm after. Why, there's *komatiks* gone all over the country after you. A lad has shot hisself down at St. Ronald's, and he's bleeding shocking.'

'All right, Jake, old friend. The turn for the path is off the big pond, is it not?'

'That's it, Doctor, but I'm coming along anyhow, 'feared I *might* be wanted.'

My little leader must have overheard this conversation, for she simply flew over the hills. Yet it was already dusk when at length we shot down the semi-precipice on the side of which the little house clings like a barnacle. The anxious crowd, gathered to await our arrival, disappeared before the avalanche, like a morning mist when the sun rises. Following directions, I found myself in a tiny, naked room, already filled with well-meaning visitors, though they were able to do nothing but look on and defile what little air made its way in through the fixed windows. Fortunately, for want of putty, air leaked in around the glass.

Stretched on the floor behind the stove lay a pale-faced boy of about ten years. His clothes had been taken off, and an old patchwork quilt covered his body. His right thigh was covered with a heterogeneous mass of bloody rags. Sitting by him was his mother, her forehead resting in her hands as if she were wrestling with some inscrutable problem. She rose as I entered with: ' 'Tis Clem, Doctor. He got Dick here to give him the gun to try and shoot a gull, and there were a high ballicater of ice in the way, and he were trying to climb up over it, and he pushed the gun before him with the bar'l turned t'wards hisself and she went off and shot him, and us doesn't know what to do next—, next, and—'

While she ran on with her story I cleared the room of visitors, and kneeling down by the boy, removed the dirty mass of rags that had been used to staunch the blood. The charge had entered the thigh at close quarters above the knee, and passed downwards, blowing the kneecap to pieces. Most of it had passed out again. The loose fragments of bone still adhering to the ragged flesh, the fragments of clothing blown into it, and the foul smell and discoloration added by the gunpowder made the outlook a very ugly one. Moreover, there rose to my mind the memory of a similar case in which we had come too late, blood poisoning having set in, and the child having died after much suffering.

The mother had by this time quieted down, and was simply repeating, 'What shall us do?'

'There's only one thing to be done. We must pack Clem up and carry him to the hospital right away.'

'Iss, Doctor, that's the only way, I'm thinking,' she replied. 'An' I suppose you'll cut off his leg, and he'll never walk no more, and Oh, dear! what—'

'Come, tear up this calico into strips and bring me some boiling water—mind, it must be well boiled; and get me that board over there —'twill serve to make a splint; and then go and tell Dick to get the dogs ready at once; for we've a Christmas tree at St. Anthony to-night, and I must be back at all costs.'

In this way we kept her too busy to worry or hesitate about letting the child go; for we well knew it was his only chance, and she had never seen a hospital, and the idea of one was as terrifying as a morgue.

'Home, home, home!' to the dogs—and once again our steel runners are humming over the crisp snow. Now in the darkness we are clinging tightly to our hand-ropes as we shoot over the hills. Now the hospital lights are coming up, and now the lights in the windows of the 'room'. As we get near they look so numerous and so cheerful that we seem to be approaching a town. Now we can hear the merry ring of the children's voices, and can make out a crowd of figures gathered around the doorway. They are waiting for the tardy arrival of 'Sandy Claws'. Of course, we are at once recognized, and there is a general hush of disappointment as if they had thought at last 'Sandy' himself was come.

'He is only a little way behind us', we shouted. 'He is coming like a whirlwind. Look out everybody when he gets here. Don't get too close to his dogs.'

Only a little while later, and the barking of dogs announces the approach of the other *komatik*. But we alone are in the secret of its real mission. Some one is calling from the darkness, and a long sleigh with a double-banked team of dogs has drawn up opposite the doorway. Two fur-clad figures standing by it, steady a huge box which is lashed upon it. The light shining on the near one reveals of his muffled face only two sparkling eyes and large icicles bristling over the muffler from heavy mustache and whiskers, like the ivory tusks of some old bull walrus. Both figures are panting with exertion, and blowing out great clouds of steam like galloping horses on a frosty morning. There could be no doubt about it, this time. Here was the real Sandy Claws at last, come mysteriously over the snows with his dogs and *komatik* and big box and all!

The excitement of the crowd, already intense from anxiety over our own delay, now knew no bounds. Where had they come from? What could be in that big box? How large it looked in the darkness! Could it have really been dragged all the way from the North Pole? Luckily, no one had the courage left to go near enough to discover the truth.

The hospital door was swung open, and a loud voice cried out: 'Welcome, welcome, Sandy Claws! We're all so glad you've come; we thought you'd forgotten us. Come right in. Come right in! Oh, no! don't think of undoing the box outside; why, you'll freeze all those toys out there! Just unlash it and bring it right in as it is. Come in;

there's a cup of tea waiting for you before you go over to start your tree growing fruit.'

There had been rumours all the week that Sandy Claws would bring his wife this year. There had been whispers even of a baby. So we could explain the second man; for the Eskimo men and women all dress alike in Labrador, which would account for Mrs. Claws' strange taste in clothes. A discreet silence was observed about her frozen whiskers.

A few minutes later another large box was carried over to the 'room'. It was full of emptiness, for the toys were on the tree long ago. But two strange masked and bewigged figures stumbled over the snow with it, to carry the little drama to its close. So complete was the faith in the unearthly origin of these our guests, that when the curtain went up more than one voice was heard to be calling out for 'Ma' and 'Dad', while a lad of several summers was found hidden under the seat, when it came his turn to go up and get his 'prize'.

And so Santa Claus came to St. Anthony, and brought a gift for us as well as presents for the children. Indeed, the best was the one he had kept for us, who had so unworthily thought that the outlook for a happy Christmas was but a poor one. Sleeping overhead, in a clean, white cot, free of pain, and with a good fighting chance for his life, lay our bright-faced lad—Clem. The gift to us this Christmas day was the chance to save his life. We would not have exchanged it for any gift we had ever heard of. At the old home, where doctors are plentiful, such a gift were impossible.

'The great life-giving gift to the world, that Christmas stands for, was to be *ours* to thus faintly re-echo on this needy, far-off shore.'

WILFRED T. GRENFELL

Anticipation

★ ★

There were the three days: the day before Christmas, the day of Christmas, and the day after. Those three days lamplight spread with a different softness over the blue-cold snow. Faces were all unlocked; thought and feeling were open and warm to the touch. Even inanimate things came close, as if they had a blood of their own running through them.

On the afternoon of the first day the cold relaxed suddenly, like a frozen rag dipped in water. Distances seemed to shrink. The dark spruce mountain moved nearer, with the bodies of the trees dark as before rain.

Martha had done up all her housework before noon, and the afternoon had the feel of Saturday. It was a parenthesis in time—before the sharp expectancy began to build with the dusk and spark to its full brightness when the lamp was lit. There were so many places it was wonderful to be that afternoon that David was scarcely still a minute.

He went outside and made a snowman. The snow was so packy it left a track right down to the grass roots. It was a perfect day to be alone with, the only confidant of its mysteries. Yet it was equally nice to be with people. The claim of their ordinary work was suspended today, no one's busyness was any kind of pushing aside.

He went inside and sat close to his grandmother. He asked her a string of questions; not for information, but because he was young and she was old. To let her feel that she was helping him get things straight was the only way he knew to give her some of the splendid feeling he had so guiltily more of.

He went out again where Chris was sawing wood. How could Chris *stand* there like that, today . . . his shoulders moved so patiently, the saw sank with such maddening slowness. Yet, because he did, he was somehow wonderful. When a block fell, David would thrust the stick ahead on the sawhorse with such a prodigal surge of helpfulness beyond what the weight of the wood asked for that Chris would have to push it back a little before he made the next cut.

He went back into the house and stood at the table where his mother was mixing doughnuts.

Everything was clean as sunshine. The yellow-shining mixing bowl in the center of the smooth hardwood bread board; the circles of pure white where the sieve had stood; the measuring cup with the flour-white stain of milk and soda on its sides; and the flat yellow-white rings of the doughnuts themselves lying beside the open-mouthed jug that held the lard, drift-smooth at the center and crinkled like pie crust along the sides. His mother carried the doughnuts to the stove, flat on her palm, and dropped them one by one into the hot fat. He followed her, watching. They'd sink to the bottom. Then, after a fascinating second of total disappearance, they'd loom dark below the surface, then float all at once, brown and hissing all over. It had never been like this, watching her make doughnuts before.

He went into the pantry and smelled the fruit cakes that lay on the inverted pans they'd been cooked in. He opened the bag of nuts and rolled one in his palm, then put it back. He put his hand deep down into the bag and rolled all the nuts through his fingers: the smooth hazelnuts that the hammer would split so precisely: the crinkled walnuts with the lung-shaped kernels so fragile that if he got one out all in one piece he'd give it to Anna: the flat black butternuts whose meat clove so tightly to the shell that if you ever got one out whole you saved it to the very last.

Then he leaned over and smelled the bag of oranges. He didn't touch it. He closed his eyes and smelled it only. The sharp, sweet, reminding, fulfilling, smell of the oranges was so incarnate of tomorrow it was delight almost to sinfulness.

He went out and sat beside Anna. She was on her knees before the lounge, turning the pages of the catalogue. They played 'Which Do You Like the Best?' with the colored pages. Anna would point to the incredibly beaded silk dress that the girl wore standing in a great stone archway with the sunlight streaming across it, as her choice. He'd say, 'Oh, I do, too.' And as his hand touched Anna's small reaching hand and as he looked at her small reaching face, he almost cried with the knowing that some Christmas Day, when he had all that money he was going to have, he'd remember every single thing that Anna had liked the best. She'd find every one of them beneath the tree when she got up in the morning.

He went out where his father was preparing the base for the tree. All the work-distraction was gone from his father today, and David knew that even if so few pieces of board were to be found as to defeat anyone else, his father would still be able to fix something that was perfect.

Joseph lay one crosspiece in the groove of the other. He said to David, 'Think you could hold her just like that, son, till I drive the nails?'

'Oh yes,' David said, 'yes.' He strove with such intense willingness to hold them so exactly that every bit of his strength and mind was soaked up. He touched the ax that would cut the tree. The bright cold touch of it shone straight through him.

He rán in to tell Anna it was almost time. He waited for her to button her gaiters. He was taut almost to pallor when Joseph stepped from the shop door, crooked the ax handle under one arm, and spat on the blade for one final touch of the whetstone.

'Chris,' he called, 'we're *goin'*!'

'All right,' Chris said. 'You go on. I guess I'll finish the wood.'

How *could* Chris stay here? How could anyone *wait* anywhere today? It was almost impossible to be still even in the place where the thing was going on.

Joseph walked straight toward the dark spruce mountain. David and Anna would fall behind, as they made imprints of their supine bodies in the snow; then run to catch up. They would rush ahead, to simulate rabbit tracks with their mittens—the palms for the parallel prints of the two back feet, the thumb the single print where the front feet struck together; then stand and wait. Their thoughts orbited the thought of the tree in the same way their bodies orbited Joseph's.

'Anna, if anyone walked right through the mountain, weeks and weeks, I wonder where he'd come out . . .'

'Dave, hold your eyes almost shut, it looks like water . . .'

'There's one, there's one . . .' But when they came to it the branches on the far side were uneven.

Joseph himself stopped to examine a tree.

'Father, the best ones are way back, ain't they?' David said quickly. This *was* a good tree, but it wouldn't be any fun if they found the perfect tree almost at once.

'There's one . . .' But it was a cat spruce.

'There's one . . .' But the spike at the top was crooked.

'There's one, Father . . .' But a squirrel's nest of brown growth spoiled the middle limbs.

Joseph found the perfect fir, just short of the mountain. The children had missed it, though their tracks were all about. He went to it from the road, straight as a die. The bottom limbs were ragged, but those could be cut off; and above them, the circlets of the upward-angling branches were perfect. The trunk was straight and round. The green of the needles was dark and rich, right to the soft-breathing tip.

'How about this one?' Joseph said.

The children said nothing, looking at the lower limbs.

'From here up,' Joseph said. He nicked the bark with his ax.

'Yes, oh yes,' they cried then. 'That's the best tree anyone could find, ain't it, Father?' The ridiculous momentary doubt of their father's judgment made them more joyous than ever.

They fell silent as Joseph tramped the snow about the base of the tree, to chop it. David made out he was shaking snow from his mitten. He took off Anna's mitten too, pretending to see if there was any snow in hers. He stood there holding her mitten-warmed hand, not saying anything, and watched his father strike the first shivering blow.

The tree made a sort of sigh as it swept through the soft air and touched the soft snow. Then the moment broke. The children came close and touched the green limbs. They thrust their faces between them—into the dark green silence. They smelled the dark green, cosy, exciting smell of the whole day in the balsam blisters on the trunk.

Joseph stood and waited: the good kind of waiting, with no older-hurry in him. Then he lifted the tree to his shoulders, both arms spread out to steady it at either end.

The twins walked close behind him. They let the swaying branches touch their faces. They walked straight now, because the first cast of dusk had begun to spread from the mountain. The first dusk-stiffening of the snow and a shadow of the first night-wonder were beginning. Now the things of the day fell behind them; because all that part of the day which could be kept warm and near was in the tree, and they were taking the tree home, into the house, where all the warm things of afterdark belonged.

Anna whispered to David, 'I got somethin for you, Dave.'

And he whispered, 'I got somethin for you, too.'

'What?'

'Oh, I can't tell.'

Then they guessed. Each guess was made deliberately small, so there'd be no chance that the other would be hurt by knowing that his present was less than the vision of it. Each of them felt that whatever they had for each other all their lives would have something of the magic, close-binding smell of the fir boughs somewhere in it, like the presents for each other of no other two people in the world.

Martha had huddled the furniture in the dining room together, to clear a corner for the tree.

'Aw, Mother,' David said, 'you said you'd wait!'

His mother laughed. 'I just moved the sofa and mats a little,' she said. 'I didn't touch the trimmings. Do you think it's too late to put them up before supper?'

'No,' David cried, 'no, I'm not a bit hungry.'

'I suppose if supper's late it'll make you late with your chores, won't it?' she said to Joseph.

'Well,' Joseph said, 'I suppose I *could* do em before supper.' He hesitated. 'Or do you want me to help you with the trimmin?'

'Oh, yes,' David said. 'Help us.'

He wanted everyone to be in on it. Especially his father. It was wonderful when his father helped them with something that wasn't work, *inside* the house.

David fanned open the great accordion-folding bell (because of one little flaw his mother had got it—it didn't seem possible—for only a quarter). He tied the two smaller bells on the hooks of the blinds. Then he and his father and Chris took off their boots. They stood on chairs in their stocking feet and hung the hemlock garlands Ellen had made; around the casings and from the four ceiling corners of the room to a juncture at its center, where the great bell was to be suspended.

Someone would say, 'Pass the scissors?' and David would say, '*Sure*,' beating with gladness to do them any small favors. Martha would stand back and say, 'A little lower on that side,' and they'd say, 'Like that? Like that? More still?' all full of that wonderful patience to make it perfect. Everyone would laugh when someone slipped off a chair.

His father would say, 'Why wouldn't some red berries look good in there?' and to hear his *father* say a thing like that filled the room with something really splendid. Sometimes he'd step on Anna's toe as they busied back and forth. He'd say, 'Oh, Anna, did that hurt?' and she'd laugh and say, 'No, it didn't hurt.' He'd say, 'Are you *sure?*' and just that would be wonderful.

The dusk thickened and the smell of the hemlock grew soft as lamplight in the room. The trimming was done and the pieces swept up and put into the stove.

Then Joseph brought in the tree, backward through the door so the limbs wouldn't break. No one spoke as he stood it in the space in the corner. It just came to the ceiling. It was perfect. Suddenly the room was whole. Its heart began to beat.

They ate in the dining room that night. David smelled the roast spare ribs that had been kept frozen in the shop. He felt now how hungry he'd been all the time.

The room was snug with the bunching of the furniture and the little splendor of eating there on a weekday. And when Martha held the match to the lamp wick, all at once the yellow lamplight soft-shadowed their faces (with the blood running warm in them after being out in the cold) like a flood and gathered the room all in from outside the windows. It touched the tree and the hemlock and the great red bell with the flaw no one could even notice, like a soft breath added to the beating of the room's heart: went out and came back with a kind of smile. The smell of the tree grew suddenly and the memory of the smell of the oranges and the feel of the nuts. In that instant suddenly, ecstatically, burstingly, buoyantly, enclosingly, sharply, safely, stingingly, watchfully, batedly, mountingly, softly, ever so softly, it was Christmas Eve.

ERNEST BUCKLER

When Heaven Smiled on Our World

Mid-winter brought our gayest, happiest times. For the *habitant* farmer of two generations back, trips and visits were special occasions, indulged in primarily during *la saison des fêtes*, the festal season, as it was, and is still, called. Originally, it meant the weeks between Christmas Day and Epiphany, inclusive, and by extension, it has stood for the season between Christmas and Lent. As the rest of our year was filled with so much work, we gaiety-loving Canadians saw to it that these eight or ten weeks had plenty of cheer and jollity. These weeks brought the only sure lull in our busy life. At this time, the harvests and their strenuous occupations were well behind us, while ploughing and seed-time still lay well ahead. The winter logging had been attended to, and a couple of months or so would elapse before sugaring-time came around again to draft the men and the horses—our only means of loco-motion then—for another ten months of ceaseless occupations. So we all turned to our yearly season of relaxation with a high zest.

Preparations were begun well in advance; in fact, during the rest of the year, everyone bore in mind the next festal season and the means to make it memorable, although this seemed to be especially the con-cern of the women. For each good housewife was anxious to have the neatest house, the prettiest and freshest rugs and bedspreads, the best-set table, the most bountiful repasts, and the most delicious dishes. Also, at least one good outfit of clothes had to be provided for each and every member of the household, so that everyone would be decently dressed during those traditional festivities. Therefore, beginning in early spring, Mother began her long-range preparations by setting apart the best loaves of maple sugar, and the jug of thickest maple syrup, then, as the year progressed, added the most luscious *confitures*, the richest jams, the clearest honey; perfect apples were set aside with the choicest vege-tables in the cellar; Father marked prime cuts of meat and fat fowls, which no one dared requisition till the appointed time; while butter, another precious reserve, lay in golden pats next to the frozen cream in the dairy-room. As the Christmas-tide drew near, milk was unfrozen for the mixing of pies, cakes, custards and *croquignoles;* these latter being rich crullers that 'kept' almost indefinitely.

The house grew redolent with the varied aromas of pastry and spices; the cupboards began to fill up with dainties; along the shelves of the cold-pantry were ranged dozens of fat meat-pies, enormous cooked hams and assorted roasts, platters of meat-balls, pigs' knuckles and sausages, not to mention big kettles of golden pea soup enriched with hulled corn and the delicate leaves of *sarriette:* this soup was frozen, then thawed as needed, being all the better for a hard freezing. In all these culinary rites, Mother was high-priestess, but Talie did her valiant share. The girls worked like young beavers too, because quantities of clothes had to be taken out of the coffers and made ready for the rounds of family parties and the usual jollifications; the best quilts were pressed and spread out on the beds, the best *catalogues* were in turn spread on the newly scrubbed floors. Meanwhile, in the out-buildings, the men-folk were no less busy. The sleighs had to be carefully inspected, polish-ed, even varnished, and the runners sharpened so that they would slide over the snow slick as grease; harness had to be gone over too, a coat of lampblack applied and the strings of bells rehung and rubbed to the ultimate shine and jingle; the fur robes were aired and brushed out; and the day before Christmas, the horses themselves were curried and combed, their manes and tails were brushed till our good steeds looked like blue-ribbon winners. And of course, sundry errands were run for the women. Finally, Father brought in a good supply of his best tobacco, which he put in a convenient place with a number of new clay pipes.

Christmas, of course, was the opening *fête-day,* although it was, for us purely a religious festival. But we thought it, and rightly, the most beautiful feast of all. It stood out from all others, with its impressive Midnight Mass at the parish church, and its *réveillon,* a special repast served on our return from church in the early morning hours.

The afternoon of December twenty-fourth saw everyone in our house occupied with our *grande toilette,* and in verifying each item of our best wearing apparel, already laid out on our beds by the careful hands of Augusta and Eloise. The men shaved and gave us young boys a haircut; the girls put up their hair in curlers; Mother was busy with a dozen things. Then came an early supper and, for us youngsters, a nap

—under protest—followed by the exciting experience of getting up and
dressing to go out practically in the middle of the night! Finally, bundled up to our ears against the sub-zero weather, we all trooped and
climbed into the sleighs, to be well wrapped up again in blankets, with
our feet resting on heated stones or on an earthenware piggin filled
with hot water. Heavy robes of buffalo or bearskin were spread over
all, allowing only our heads to protrude, and off we went at last, for a
five-mile ride in the open sleighs to the plateau above, all the sleighbells
jingling sweetly in the night. Other bells answered merrily up and
down the roads, heralding relatives and friends likewise converging
towards the village which stood like a lighted beacon above the plain.
And at last our happy, excited group entered the church.

How lovely it looked to our eyes, the church on Christmas night!
It had beckoned to us from afar, brightly glowing on its pedestal of
pure white snow, under a cobalt sky, its graceful spire apparently in
touch with the stars. Our eyes unconsciously searched for the Star of
Bethlehem, but only inside did we find it, shining over the *crèche* where
a dimpled, smiling, waxen Babe reposed on straw . . . The church
interior was redolent with the smell of pine and balsam trees sheltering
the *crèche;* candles were blazing on the altar, and our *curé* entered the
sanctuary clad in vestments of white and gold, while from the back of
the church the choir in their vestments came down the central aisle,
singing a Christmas hymn.

That choir! . . . We had met it as we came in, and its members were
all *a-bustle.* I use the word advisedly. I said that it was a vested choir,
but this term needs qualifying. Its members could hardly afford to have
expensive cassocks made in town, so our choristers—all boys and men,
some of them mustachioed and bearded—wore long, full skirts of black
sateen adjusted, more or less, with drawstrings. Over the skirts fell full
white surplices, each one a mantle of charity, for almost invariably the
skirts were put on askew, hiking up in front or trailing in the back,
with the drawstrings tied in clumsy knots. But so true is it that beauty
lies principally in the eyes of the beholders, that most of us were quite
oblivious of the misfit vestments worn by our choristers: all we saw
was a group of earnest parishioners marching devoutly down the aisle
and singing with all their hearts an old Christmas carol:

> Minuit, chrétiens,
> C'est l'heure solennelle
> Qu'un Dieu Sauveur
> Descendit parmi nous . . .
> Noël, Noël, voici le Rédempteur!
> Noël, Noël, voici le Rédempteur! . . .

When the choristers had ranged themselves in the sanctuary, the *curé* began the Mass. We bowed our heads in unison with his, but our hearts were uplifted. And soon the choir intoned the beautiful old hymn, 'Come all ye faithful', in Latin:

> Adeste, fideles,
> Laeti triumphantes;
> Venite, venite
> In Bethlehem . . .

Then came the reading of the Gospel in French, our pastor amplifying on that theme, the beauty of which we country folk could so well understand: an anxious and unworldly villager looking for shelter at night in a strange town; then a tender young mother clasping close her new-born son; a Child tiny yet mighty as are all babes, He mightiest yet lowliest of all; and simple shepherds watching over flocks by night, and fair angels singing a wondrous song; a song the choristers now took up:

> Gloria in excelsis Deo,
> Et in terra pax . . .

'*Pax*' . . . Here was another nice word, I told myself. Sort of complete and yet easy to say. *Pax* . . . I must ask Grandfather just what it meant . . . But when Mass ended, we all stopped at the *crèche* in its bower of evergreens, and looked at the sweet Babe on the clean straw, at the figures of Mary and Joseph, of the ox and the ass, and in the distance, the shepherds coming, with tiny woolly sheep trailing behind . . . We children could have stayed there for an hour, but the grown-ups thought of the patient horses standing out in the cold, and of the warm house waiting; so we were dragged out to the sleighs, while, from all around us, voices called out in greeting:

'*Heureux Noël! Joyeux Noël!*'—'Merry Christmas! Merry Christmas!'

The restive horses had been eager to start, and we were soon whisked

CORINNE ROCHELEAU ROULEAU

out of the village and speeding over frozen roads, down the steep in-
cline to the valley below, in a perfect jangle of sleigh-bells. Farm dogs
barked excitedly as we sped by, and every house was brightly lit, sending out golden shafts from its windows onto the gleaming stretches of
snow outside. And now we were home again, sleepy and cold and
hungry too, but soon comforted by the hot *réveillon.* After which we
tumbled into bed, happy in the realization that the festal season had
been auspiciously launched at last . . . Oh, Christmas night! Most
beautiful night in all the year! . . .

Christmas morning was almost the only one in the year when we all
got up late. For us, there were no bulging stockings hanging from the
fireplace mantel, no Christmas tree twinkled anywhere in the house:
but as these were not yet a traditional part of our celebration, we did
not miss them. Our time to exchange gifts and good wishes was New
Year's Day, and it was but a week off. Christmas, for us, was a nice,
long, restful day in which to talk of the night's happenings, to sing old
French carols, of which we had an extensive repertoire. We loved and
sang them all; but perhaps because of its imagery, we liked the following one:

> D'où viens-tu, bergère,
> D'où viens-tu?
> Je viens de l'étable,
> De m'y promener;
> J'ai vu un miracle
> Ce soir arrivé.

CORINNE ROCHELEAU ROULEAU

Magi on Snowshoes

‹‹

Many years ago, before the days of airplanes and radios, the Christmas season came to the little town of Albany on James Bay. There was a settlement at the mouth of the greatest northern river in Ontario. There were only three mails a year. One was brought through Hudson Strait from Scotland in August on the sailing ship which carried all the supplies from the outside world. A canoe made a round trip of a thousand miles in June and September. It was the twilight of the 250-year reign of the Hudson's Bay Company. There was a white church in the village. The Indians lived in birch-bark wigwams. The company's fort was like a feudal castle dominating the scene.

It was the hunting season; most of the families were far away. Two days before the Birth of Christ, a missionary standing on the bank saw something like a black serpent winding its way down the slope a mile away. It was a Cree family on the march. The man, breaking a trail on snowshoes, led the way; behind came his wife with a baby on her back. There were four starved dogs hauling a toboggan. Two or three half-grown children brought up the rear. They settled down in half an hour, after travelling three days through the woods at 30 degrees below zero. One thing brought them: Like the magi of old, they came to see a sign.

By Christmas Eve there were a hundred tents around the church. In the meantime the interior was transformed. A cedar tree was nailed to the end of each pew, a silver star made from a new tin plate hung on a wire from the ceiling, incredible flowers were fashioned by deft hands from colored paper so that the aisle looked like the Celestial City. The floors were scrubbed; the box stove shone like black marble.

On Christmas morning, while it was yet dark, the church was filled— the men on one side, the women on the other. Every man wore new embroidered moccasins, and every woman wore a new tartan shawl. They sang in a strange language songs that had been heard in Europe in the Middle Ages. It was a moving thing to see the silent faces of bronze listening to the wondrous tale. To them the manger was lined with spruce boughs like their own wigwams. They had never seen sheep. They pictured wild deer of the forest peering through the trees. It was a snowshoe trail they saw stretching far to the East whence the Medicine Men came. But it was an authentic Christmas. There was an inner peace and joy on that lonely shore.

Next day the children had their hour. A tree stood in the schoolhouse lighted with three inches of wax candle wedged in a hundred rifle cartridges tied to the branches. A bag of candies which shone like rubies, topaz and emeralds waited for every child. A blue goose frozen in its feathers hung high for the oldest grandmother.

The octave ended on New Year's Day, the state festival. The ancient Scottish tradition of the old company was solemnly observed. It was the custom for every Indian to call at the factory and the mission. An anxious bachelor and his dog driver surveyed the ammunition, a bag of flour, a tub of lard, a box of currants, brown sugar and a chest of gunpowder tea. All night long the mud oven was fired. At 10 o'clock in the morning the procession started. Tea flowed in gallons. The path on the river bank between the church and the old factory was as smooth as the Queen Elizabeth Highway. That night the northern lights came out to serenade the stars.

> Dear God, they shone in Palestine
>   Like this, and yon pale moon serene
> Looked down among the lowly kine,
>   On Mary and the Nazarene.
> The angels called from deep to deep,
>   The burning heavens felt the thrill,
> Startling the flocks of silly sheep
>   And lonely shepherds on the hill.

In the morning the tents were down. The mystic visitors were gone. 'They departed unto their own home another way.'

ROBERT J. RENISON

Frostbound, 1937

Last night when we went to bed the windows on the inside were covered with frost an inch thick; the logs in the walls and the shakes in the roof, cracked like gunshots, as they were split by the cold; and out on the lake the ice kept up an almost steady booming, interspersed with the horrid ripping and tearing that always makes my spine tingle. During the night I was waked repeatedly by such terrific cracks in the logs that I thought the cabin was coming down on our heads. When the temperature is falling, we expect a drop of 15 or 25 degrees during the night, beginning at sunset, but last night it broke all records.

This morning I was the first one out of bed . . . It was still dark outside; dawn had not yet begun although it was long past eight. The windows were so densely frosted that it seemed as if daylight, even if it were there, could never penetrate the cabin. I lit the lamp then carefully laid the pile of shavings, as always unfailingly prepared by J. the evening before, in the front of the stove and applied a match. After which I delicately laid on more shavings and then larger and larger sticks. Everything was ice cold and I was careful not to touch any metal with bare hands, having learned from bitter experience that skin, especially moist skin, freezes fast and is sometimes peeled right off at the slightest contact with very cold metal. Still clad in bathrobe and slippers, I went to scrape away the frost and read the thermometer outside. I realized then that, although I didn't feel chilled, I could hardly move my arms.

'I'll just see what the temperature is *inside* first,' I thought, and went to peer at the thermometer hanging above our dining-table. It read 25 below. Gosh! That couldn't be right! How could we sleep like that, how could I be wandering around with only a wrapper on? I *must* see what it was outside!

I couldn't even find the mercury. It dawned on me, after a time, that it had gone its limit and jammed at 50 below. My exclamations roused J. and we were so busy arguing over the thermometer that we forgot to say 'Merry Christmas'. I was convinced that if the mercury could have gone below 50 it would have read at least 60 below. J. said it was not much colder than 50; that he could tell from past experience in the Arctic just how many degrees the temperature drops when it gets beyond 45 below. For one thing, if it is 55 or more below, when hot water is poured out of a window, it freezes solid before it reaches the snow level. I could hardly wait until we had hot water to try this experiment. Sure enough—when, later, I poured a stream from the tea-kettle onto the snow outside, the water steamed and twisted into threads, but did not actually turn solid till it reached the ground. We must put out our unused thermometer whose scale goes to 60 below.

By the time dawn was coming we had scraped two peepholes in the frost on the panes; and we stood quiet to watch the winter sunrise. The radiant peaks of the Driftwood Mountains, cut like white icing into pinnacles and rims against the apple-green sky, were brushed with pink, that, even as we watched, spread down and down and turned to gold. Rays of the rising sun, coming between the pointed firs of the east shore, stretched straight across the white lake, and as they touched it huge crystals, formed by the intense cold, burst into sparkling scintillating light. The snow-bowed trees of the south and west shores were hung with diamonds; and finally the willows around our cabin were decked with jewels as large as robins' eggs that flashed red and green and blue. No Christmas trees decorated by human hands were ever so exquisite as the frosted trees of this northern forest. The sky turned to deep, deep blue, and the white world burst into dazzling, dancing colours as the sun topped the forest . . .

Then, suddenly, outside came a burst of rippling notes. *Birds,* singing a clear, sweet song! . . . By the open water patch below our bank were three fat little grey dippers, or water ouzels, with short bobbing tails . . . Their song echoed back and forth so that all the lake was ringing with it . . .

For a distance of at least thirty yards from shore where the deep springs gush out under the banks, the lake is still unfrozen. The temperature of the water doesn't seem to be affected by the temperature of the air. The water stays at 38 degrees F. whether the thermometer outside our cabin reads 32 above or 50 below. Here the dippers swim and dive and hunt for insects, or float in the water like miniature ducks . . . When they tire of swimming or feeding, they fly high in the air, over our cabin or over the forest, singing as they go and chasing each other in endless games. And they spiral down from the sky, showering music like the English skylarks . . .

No European nightingale, singing in a hot, lush summer evening, ever wove the spell of enchantment that the dippers did with those crystal tinkles, which matched so perfectly the icy purity of the winter . . . (singers) undismayed by a cold that froze all other living things . . .

Our first Christmas Day in the wilderness was upon us.

After a breakfast of canned grapefruit which we had been saving especially, and pancakes with the last of our syrup, also preserved scrupulously for Christmas, we did our usual chores. I cleaned the cabin and began a round of baking. In addition to bannock, which I bake daily either in the drum oven or in an open fry pan on top of the stove, I made tarts of strawberry jam and a chocolate cake. As these favourite articles of diet make inroads on a meager supply of crisco, jam, and sugar, we have them only for very special celebrations . . .

We had our Christmas dinner at five: dehydrated potatoes and onions and a bit of moose steak, especially saved and tendered, baked in a pan with stuffing. For dessert there were the jam tarts and chocolate cake. With these, vanished the last vestiges of Christmas, the things which made it a little different from other days.

THEODORA C. STANWELL-FLETCHER

Edna Eldorado

▲ ▲
● ●

During my first visit to the Klondike I heard the story of the three young miners, John Lind, David Skeffington Mitchell and William Wilkinson, who found a treasure far exceeding in value all the gold-dust they had washed out of Claim Number Eleven on Eldorado Creek.

They had been to Dawson, fifteen miles, with their dog-team, and with their sled heavily laden were on their way back through the dark and creaking cold. Thirty miles of travel had wearied both dogs and men, and before tackling the last mile or two they paused for a breathing spell not far from a cabin which had long been deserted.

Out of the glittering, starry silence came a low moaning sound, and while the three stood wondering they perceived a dim light in the home-made, gin-bottle window of the cabin. With the comment that there was no gol-darned sense about a light in that place, Johnny led the way towards it while the dogs were left to huddle down on the trail.

He pulled open the door and entered. The moans were coming from a bunk where a young woman lay, but they were now pitiably weak. Coming close to the bunk with the candle in his hand, he took one look and then cried, 'My God, boys! There's a new-born baby! Bill, run back to the sled and get that bottle of brandy.'

The other two stood by the bunk chafing the cold hands of the mother, whose strength was all but gone and on whose face purple circles were already gathering about the eyes and mouth. The fire was made up, snow was melted for hot water, an attempt was made to give the mother a teaspoonful of brandy, but she was past swallowing, and as they looked she gave a last quivering sigh and was gone.

'What in the name of God are we three to do?' asked Johnny, after reverently covering the body of the young girl-mother with an old blanket. He sat down on the stump of a tree which served as a chair in the cabin and looked at the other two in utter dismay.

Bill, who had received lately from friends in England a suit of soft woollen underwear, began to undress. Without a word he pulled the shirt over his head and handed it to Dave, who wrapped it about the child, saying softly, 'It's a girl baby.' The warmth stilled the infant's wailing, and there the three sat in a silence that could be felt.

'There's someone coming outside now!' said Bill. 'It sounds like a team of dogs; I can hear the runners on the snow.'

In the next minute the door burst open and a young man dashed into the room.

'Here I am, Jen, old girl!' he called out. 'I met the Mounted Police doctor on the way up Bonanza. He'll take care of you, my dear.'

Then he started back when he saw the three men. The baby began to cry feebly. Then, rushing to the bunk, pulling away the blanket, the husband saw the still form there and with a moan sank on the floor.

The doctor stepped into the cabin, looked at the young mother, listened for the heart-beats and, straightening himself, shook his head. Then he took the baby from Dave's arms and asked hurried questions.

'Where do you boys live?' he asked.

'About a mile farther up the creek, at Number Eleven,' answered Johnny.

'Any women about?'

'Not right here. There are about sixteen on Eldorado and Bonanza creeks,' said Bill.

'Can you get any of them to-night?'

'Don't think so.'

'You fellows will have to take care of the poor little wretch yourselves. I'll write out some directions for you.'

As he wrote he added, 'You might put two or three drops of brandy in with the tinned milk and hot water, and give the child a few spoonfuls every three hours. The poor little thing hasn't much chance of life. Can you manage?'

'Yes,' stoutly answered Bill. 'I fed one of the nippers at home once when he was ill.'

'Well,' continued the doctor, 'Find something to wrap the baby in, and if ever you got speed out of those dogs, do it now. I'll come in to see you in the morning, and attend to matters here.' The doctor motioned towards the bunk and the limp figure lying beside it.

They found some of the mother's clothes hanging on the wall, and these, very awkwardly, they wrapped around the baby. Bill went out and got some blankets he had just bought in Dawson, and after warming them by the stove put them in a packing-box which he had picked up in the cabin. He laid the baby in the box and drew the blankets carefully over it. This he carried out and fastened on the least-exposed part of the sled. Then with Johnny and Dave helping the dogs to pull, and Bill guarding the box, they started on the run for their own cabin. Never had so strange a load gone along the Eldorado trail, or any other trail, for that matter, as went that Christmas Eve—the dog-team, the three men and the baby, while the northern stars shone brightly on their pathway.

At the cabin of the three strapping nurses, the fire was quickly lighted and the baby, still sleeping, was carefully laid on one of the home-made cots. Soon water was boiling and, following the doctor's directions, Bill prepared the baby's food.

Meanwhile Dave and Johnny had cooked the supper, to which they all drew up their stools. Just as they were finishing, the baby gave a little cry, so Bill, having her food in an old tin cup on the stove, took her up while Johnny and Dave cleared away the supper dishes—three tin cups, three tin plates and the frying-pan.

'I'll take the first shift,' said Bill, who had constituted himself shift-boss. Johnny fetched a new candle and stuck it in the candlestick, an empty beer bottle. Then he and Dave went over to their beds and were soon asleep.

Bill, having lulled the little creature, who now seemed contented and happy, was walking up and down with her in his arms, softly humming to himself one of the old Christmas carols, brought to his mind by the strangely beautiful incidents of the night. Almost he heard again the old cathedral chimes at home—Silent Night, Holy Night.

Next morning Dave harnessed the dogs in preparation for gathering in the women along the creek in order to find someone who would volunteer to care for the baby. By this time the boys had appointed themselves official guardians; this was *their* baby.

'You boys be all ready when the women arrive, and a lot of the fellows will be coming along just to see the kid,' said Dave proudly, as he drew on his cap and mittens.

When the women, all excited by the news, began pouring into the cabin, a difficulty arose. Every one of the sixteen wanted the baby. Bill,

Dave and Johnny sat in judgment, listening to each woman's claim.

'What were you on the "outside"?' asked Dave of each, while the other two listened gravely to the answers.

'I was a cook in a hotel.'

'I was a dressmaker.'

'A schoolteacher.'

'I was a stenographer.'

So it went, the three wise judges weighing carefully the special qualifications which each woman seemed to have. Ten applicants had appeared before them when an older woman shoved forward, saying, 'I minded my own business and looked after my husband, and wasn't wasting my time answering impudent questions from young idiots like you three. Hand that poor little innocent to me, and you boys get busy and collect the dust to buy milk for her.'

She walked over to the bed and picked up the baby with wise, motherly hands. Many present knew of the little grave she had left in distant Nova Scotia and all conceded her natural right to have the child.

By this time the cabin was packed to the door. One man after another, drawing out his poke of gold-dust, emptied part of it into the dish that Johnny was passing around. Dave brought out the scales and found that they had twenty-five ounces of dust, current value, four hundred dollars. It was needed, with fresh cow's milk at two dollars a pint, and very scarce at that. Soon things were settled and Mrs. Brock, who was working the next claim with her husband, was escorted to her cabin, where she soon had the child in more comfortable clothing.

When the doctor arrived he reported the child's father very ill with pleurisy. If he recovered, he would be sent to his home. The tale was like many others in the Klondike. This boy and girl from the Middle West, after reading the glowing accounts of the great discovery, had decided to follow the gold-rush. They married and started off on the adventure. Between them they had enough money to get to Skagway. From there on the faith and endurance of strong bodies and strong souls was necessary, which neither of them had. They had drifted from one place and one job to another until at last Jennie was taken ill, and the young husband, able to work but little in the Arctic climate, had no place but the deserted cabin on Eldorado Creek for a temporary shelter where their child might be born.

And so the Christmas baby grew under Mrs. Brock's motherly care, and was the pet of Eldorado Creek, though Johnny, Dave and Bill oversaw particularly her care and what they called her education.

In the Spring, just before the clean-up on the claims, Bill remarked to Dave, 'Say, the mater would have a fit if that child weren't baptized.'

'Why can't she be?' answered Dave. 'The weather is warmer, and we could take her in to Dawson next Sunday.'

After a great deal of fuss and consultation, in which almost every man and woman on the creek joined, they all decided to go to Dawson next Sunday. What would the baby be called? All sorts of fancy names were suggested—Marjorie, Myrtle, Gwendolyn, but these were discarded as unfitting. As to the plain names, none could be agreed on.

'She must have a Klondike name,' said Dave, 'Real Klondike.'

'What's the matter with Bonanza?' said someone.

'You darned idiots,' said Mrs. Brock. 'Fasten such a name on my wee lamb? I won't have it.'

'Anyway, it's got to be Eldorado,' declared someone, 'for she was the first child born on the creek.'

Bill, after some moments of quiet thought, looked up, 'How about Edna Eldorado?' he said.

'That's it,' shouted the others.

Early Sunday morning all Eldorado Creek was astir. Such a procession as there was, and how it grew as it passed The Forks, and went up Bonanza Creek to Dawson! The little Presbyterian log church couldn't hold all the people who wanted to see the dedication of the first Klondike baby.

Johnny, Dave and Bill, carefully shaved and in their best 'outside' clothes, stood with the baby in front of the Communion Table. When the parson lifted the little child so that all could see the little, fluffy, golden head, and said solemnly, 'Edna Eldorado, I baptize thee—' there were few dry eyes in the church, for the story of the child was known to them all; how Bill, Dave and Johnny had been led by the Christmas star to 'the place where the young child was'.

EDITH TYRRELL

St. Nick Flies the Oil Flare Trail

★ ★ ★ ★ ★ ★ ★ ★ ★ ★ ★ ★ ★ ★ ★ ★ ★ ★ ★

It's Christmas Eve in the Arctic.

It's been Christmas Eve for weeks.

Christmas Eve that stretches unbroken through Christmas, and Christmas Night. Unbroken for days past. Unbroken for days to come.

Tomorrow, only the dim flickering of a feeble two-hour twilight will glimmer weakly in the sky to crack the long black and grey hours and herald Christmas day to a hundred weathermen who man the observation posts dotted across the ice of Canada's northern rim.

Scattered along the Arctic Archipelago, from 1,500 to 2,000 miles straight north from Ottawa, tiny groups of men in a score of weather stations will huddle in their snow-bound huts and for a few moments break the endless silence of the Arctic as they send their radio reports of weather conditions whispering south along the shortwave bands. Then, their task for the day done, they will sign off again, to be lost once more for 24 hours in the icy stillness of millions of square miles of snow.

' 'Twas the night before Christmas when all through the house
Not a creature was stirring, not even a mouse . . .'

For the past week the long northern Christmas Eve has been dotted with beacons of fire. Tiny sparkling flames, lost in the vast reaches of ice, have been twinkling hopefully into the sky.

Blazing oil drums set out on the ice mark the weather station 'chimneys' which Santa must visit. The flames must be carefully fed by the watchers so that the RCAF navigators in aircraft cruising high above can pick them out and guide the pilots in for the Christmas 'drop' to the men waiting anxiously below.

'The stockings were hung by the chimney with care
In hopes that St. Nicholas soon would be there . . .'

On the packed and tumbled ice, a half dozen men, snugly clad in heavy parkas, hoods pulled up over their faces, stamp their feet and beat their mittened hands together. Their thoughts are fastened on the four or five heavy canvas bags that will come streaking down from the moonlit sky, tossed from the belly of a four-motored North Star roaring only 50 feet overhead.

Mail, gifts, and food. Particularly food. Turkey, plum pudding, and Christmas cake for appetites sharpened by the biting cold and weeks of nothing but canned food for breakfast, lunch and supper since fresh supplies from the last 'drop' ran out.

> 'The children were nestled all snug in their beds
> While visions of sugar plums danced in their heads . . .'

Beside them, whining and shivering in the 50-below temperature, are the teams of huskies harnessed to the sleds, ready to race across the ice to retrieve the precious bundles, and drag them painfully back across the snow fields to the distant huts.

> 'And Mamma in her kerchief and I in my cap
> Had just settled down for a long Winter's nap . . .'

Because 'day-time' is nothing but a faint glimmer in the sky, the drops are made by the light of the 'midnight sun', with the moon's reflection on the snow dimly lighting the operation. While some of the bundles are dropped by parachute, the majority of them are just thrown overboard to fall freely into the snow below, and so the plane must throttle down to the lowest possible speed, about 140 mph for a North Star, and come in over the drop area no more than 50 feet above the ground.

Over Canada's rugged northern terrain, where snow-covered mountains frequently rise whitely from snow-covered plains to a height of 6,000 feet, this is a tricky operation which needs all the light possible. If clouds obscure the moonlight, the drop must be postponed. Last week the RCAF completed eight of ten scheduled drops. Poor weather and lack of moonlight however caused the drops at Pond Inlet, on Northern Baffin Island, and at Craig Harbor, on Ellesmere Island, to be postponed until the full moon in January.

> 'The moon on the breast of the new-fallen snow
> Gave the lustre of midday to objects below . . .'

The US Air Force also made some drops to Canadian weather stations to help out the RCAF. Among others, they did the drops at the two most northerly stations, Eureka, on Ellesmere Island, just 10 degrees from the Pole, and the most northern one of all, Alert, just 600 miles from the Pole.

From Goose Bay, RCAF Dakotas swung over the north-east coast of Labrador to Cape Hope's Advance, Resolution Island, Nottingham Island, and Cape Dorset, all of them lying north of the Hudson Strait, itself some 1,000 miles north of Ottawa's latitude.

The other drops, to Isaachen, Arctic Bay, and Mould Bay, lying far north of Baffin Island, some 1,500 miles north of Ottawa, were made by the giant North Stars, with their four mighty engines pounding through the frigid Arctic skies.

> 'When what to my wondering eyes should appear
> But a miniature sleigh, and eight tiny reindeer . . .'

Most difficult part of the operation is to find the isolated stations at all. Navigation is fantastically difficult over the trackless white terrain that stretches unbroken below, where it is almost impossible to tell even if the plane is over land or water. Painstaking calculations, grim-eyed searches for almost non-existent landmarks, and tense minutes of waiting plague the crews guiding the aircraft.

> 'With a little old driver so lively and quick
> I knew in a moment it must be Saint Nick . . .'

The North Stars of 426 Squadron, who made the most northern drops, check out of Dorval Airport loaded with every pound of weight they can carry, and roar pole-wards into the glow of the northern lights at well over 200 mph.

> 'More rapid than eagles his coursers they came . . .'

Even though it is a special plane, the take-off follows the normal routine. After checking his Christmas cargo to make sure everything is secure, the pilot moves into the cockpit, and there, with the co-pilot and the flight engineer runs through the long 'cockpit check' of every instrument. Outside the ground-crew stand by on the frost-dusted runway with fire extinguishers waiting for the motors to start, each in its proper turn.

'Port inner!' shouts the pilot.

'All clear!' comes the answer, and the first engine revs slowly into life.

As it catches hold, the ritual is repeated for the other motors: 'Starboard inner! Port outer! Starboard outer!'

As the 'all-clears' sound back, each prop begins to whirl.

'And he whistled, and shouted and called them by name:
Now Dasher! Now, Dancer! Now Prancer and Vixen!
On, Comet! On, Cupid! On, Donner and Blitzen! . . .'

Then begins the complicated patter between the pilot and control tower, involving taxi clearances, runway clearance, briefing details of wind velocity, ceiling, weather fronts, other air traffic, flight plan, and finally, take-off clearance 'for non-stop to Churchill, at 5,000 feet'.

The big ship swings on to the main runway, hurtles itself forward between the twin rows of runway lights until its giant wings bite the air, and it lifts and plunges into the darkness.

'To the top of the porch, to the top of the wall!
Now, dash away! Dash away! Dash away, all!'

Clawing for height, it thunders north toward Churchill where it will stop over and refuel before heading into the Arctic. Roaring over the towns of the Ottawa Valley, leaving the lights of civilization behind, it drones on through the night with its crew and burden of Christmas cheer for men who have been marooned in their isolated stations as long as two years.

'So up to the housetop the coursers they flew
With a sleigh full of toys and St. Nicholas too . . .'

For the men of the detachment, bundled against the wind, anxiously waiting beside the flaming oil drums, the first contact they have had with the outer world except by radio for months, is heralded by the ear-blasting roar of the engines, as the plane swoops down to examine the drop area, and make a practice run.

'And then in a twinkling I heard on the roof
The prancing and pawing of each little hoof . . .'

After checking the wind speed and direction, the pilot orders the 'drop crew' to stand by at the rear door of the plane. Since the bundles must be dropped accurately to avoid hitting people on the ground or losing them in deep snow, the first drop is always a tense moment for both aircrew and weathermen.

When the pilot has made his decision on the best approach angle, he throttles back the engines and runs in as low as possible. Then, at the proper instant, he shouts the drop signal, and the men at the rear instantly kick out the first two bundles which plunge down toward the group below.

'As I drew in my head and was turning around,
Down the chimney Saint Nicholas came with a bound . . .'

As the last of the bundles fall, the whole detachment, including Eskimos and Eskimo children, run forward to retrieve them. Flung helter-skelter over a half-mile of ice are all their new supplies, fresh clothing, Christmas letters, Christmas parcels, Christmas dinners, and even a Christmas tree.

'A bundle of toys he had flung on his back,
And he looked like a peddler just opening his pack . . .'

Preparing the bundles for the drop started many months ago. Last October the Department of Transport notified each family concerned that a Christmas delivery would be made by the RCAF and mail must be in their hands by mid-November.

The RCAF personnel then parcel all the gifts in special heavy canvas containers used for dropping purposes, and because the majority are 'free-dropped' the wrapping must be securely done if they are not to be damaged. After they are properly bundled, they are flown to assembly points ready to be picked up by the aircraft and flown into the North about mid-December.

'He spoke not a word but went straight to his work,
And filled all the stockings; then turned with a jerk . . .'

Their long task done, the crew in the North Star circle the drop area, watching the excited group below gather up their bundles before they point the nose of their aircraft south and start the long flight homewards.

'And laying his finger aside of his nose,
And giving a nod, up the chimney he rose . . .'

Finally, when all the bundles are collected, the ground party gather in a circle on the ice to wave a final, wordless farewell to the men in the plane. The radio operator calls the weather station operator below, picks up the latest weather forecast for the return trip, and signs off with:

'Breaking contact. Happy Christmas everyone. Over, and out!'

'He sprang to his sleigh, to his team gave a whistle,
And away they all flew like the down of a thistle.
But I heard him exclaim ere he drove out of sight,
'Happy Christmas to all, and to all a good night!'

JOHN DALRYMPLE

Boarder's Christmas, 1944

Ice in the River at Montreal,
Late ships scurrying past Quebec,
Sydney sighing, 'That's nearly all!'
Louisburg waiting her turn on deck,
Convoys crowding in Halifax,
Winter loading in old St. John—
These are the signs on the ocean tracks
That Christmas is coming on.

Cold the wind through the Newfie gate,
Wet the wind on the Rupert shore,
Fog in the Juan de Fuca Strait
Sets Victoria's horn a-snore.
At Vancouver the running gear
Prattles low while the rigging drips,
But the ancient spell of a midnight clear
Settles upon the ships.

Here at anchorage, trot and dock,
Great ships, mean ships—the old, the new—
Wait the launches that lunge and rock
Their friendly way with the Boarding crew—
The hardy pilgrims who break the chill
Of the toughest tramp in the farthest berth;
Men of war, but their message still
Peace and good will on earth.

Theirs no glory of sword and fire
Who meet their foe in the muddled mind,
In the fearful heart and the cold desire
Of the witting deaf and the knowing blind;
But the ships going out to the rendezvous
Are their battle honours, their rich reward,
And they know a hope that the shepherds knew
Who saw the infant Lord.

LIEUT.-COMMANDER FREDERICK B. WATT

Spirit
of Christmas
Past

Dawn and Diamonds

Two days before Christmas the ground was still bare. I had a splendid new cutter with a top and side curtains; a heavy outfit, but one that would stand up, I believed, under any road conditions. I was anxious to use it, too, for I intended to spend a two weeks' holiday up north with my family. I was afraid, if I used the buggy, I might find it impossible to get back to town, seeing that the first heavy winter storms usually set in about the turn of the year.

School had closed at noon. I intended to set out next morning at as early an hour as I could. I do not know what gave me my confidence, but I firmly expected to find snow on the ground by that time. I am rather a student of the weather. I worked till late at night getting my cutter ready. I had to adjust my buggy pole and to stow away a great number of parcels. The latter included the first real doll for my little girl, two or three picture books, a hand sleigh, Pip—a little stuffed dog of the silkiest fluffiness—and as many more trifles for wife and child as my Christmas allowance permitted me to buy. It was the first time in the five years of my married life that, thanks to my wife's cooperation in earning money, there was any Christmas allowance to spend; and since I am writing this chiefly for her and the little girl's future reading, I want to set it down here, too, that it was thanks to this very same co-operation that I had been able to buy the horses and the driving outfit which I needed badly, for the poor state of my health forbade more rigorous exercise. I have already said, I think, that I am essentially an outdoor creature; and for several years the fact that I had been forced to look at the out-of-doors from the window of a town house only, had been eating away at my vitality. Those drives took decades off my age, and in spite of incurable illness my few friends say that I look once more like a young man.

Besides my Christmas parcels I had to take oats along, enough to feed the horses for two weeks. And I was, as I said, engaged that evening in stowing everything away, when about nine o'clock one of the physicians of the town came into the stable. He had had a call into the country, I believe, and came to order a team. When he saw me working in the shed, he stepped up and said, 'You'll kill your horses.' 'Meaning?' I queried. 'I see you are getting your cutter ready,' he replied. 'If I were you, I should stick to the wheels.' I laughed. 'I might not be able to get back to work.' 'Oh yes,' he scoffed, 'it won't snow up before the end of next month. We figure on keeping the cars going for a little while yet.' Again I laughed. 'I hope not,' I said, which may not have sounded very gracious.

At ten o'clock every bolt had been tightened, the horses' harness and their feed were ready against the morning, and everything looked good to me.

I was going to have the first real Christmas again in twenty-five years, with a real Christmas tree, and with wife and child; and even though it was a poor man's Christmas, I refused to let anything darken my Christmas spirit or dull the keen edge of my enjoyment. Before going out, I stepped into the office of the stable, slipped a half-dollar into the hostler's palm and asked him once more to be sure to have the horses fed at half-past five in the morning.

Then I left. A slight haze filled the air, not heavy enough to blot out the stars, but sufficient to promise hoarfrost at least. Somehow there was no reason to despair as yet of Christmas weather.

I went home and to bed and slept about as soundly as I could wish. When the alarm of my clock went off at five in the morning, I jumped out of bed and hurried down to shake the fire into activity. As soon as I had started something of a blaze, I went to the window and looked out. It was pitch dark, of course, the moon being down by this time, but it seemed to me that there was snow on the ground. I lighted a lamp and held it to the window; and sure enough, its rays fell on white upon white on shrubs and fence posts and window ledge. I laughed and instantly was in a glow of impatience to be off.

At half-past five, when the coffee water was in the kettle and on the stove, I hurried over to the stable across the bridge. The snow was three inches deep, enough to make the going easy for the horses. The slight haze persisted, and I saw no stars. At the stable I found, of course, that the horses had not been fed; so I gave them oats and hay and went to call the hostler. When after much knocking at last he responded to my impatience, he wore a guilty look on his face but assured me that he was just getting up to feed my team. 'Never mind about feeding,' I said. 'I've done that. But have them harnessed and hitched up by a quarter past six. I'll water them on the road.' They never drank their fill before nine o'clock. And I hurried home to get my breakfast . . .

'Merry Christmas!' the hostler called after me; and I shouted back over my shoulder, 'The same to you.' The horses were going under the merry jingle of the bells which they carried for the first time this winter . . .

We flew along—the road seemed ideal—the air was wonderfully crisp and cold—my cutter fulfilled the highest expectations—the horses revelled in speed. But soon I pulled them down to a trot, for I followed the horsemen's rules whenever I could, and Dan, as I mentioned, was any way rather too keen at the start for steady work later on. I settled back. The top of my cutter was down, for not a breath stirred, and I was always anxious to see as much of the country as I could . . .

Do you know which is the stillest hour of the night? The hour before dawn. It is at that time, too, that in our winter nights the mercury dips down to its lowest level. Perhaps the two things have a causal relation—whatever there is of wild life in nature, withdraws more deeply within itself; it curls up and dreams . . .

The stillest hour! In starlit winter nights the heavenly bodies seem to take on an additional splendour, something next to blazing, overweening boastfulness. 'Now sleeps the world,' they seem to say, 'but we are awake and weaving destiny.' And on they swing on their immutable paths . . .

We drove along—and slowly, slowly came the dawn. You could not define how it came. The whole world seemed to pale and whiten, and that was all. There was no sunrise. It merely seemed as if all of Nature—very gradually—was soaking itself full of some light; it was dim at first, but never grey; and then it became the whitest, the clearest, the most undefinable light. There were no shadows. Under the brush of the wild land which I was skirting by now there seemed to be quite as much of luminosity as overhead. The mist was the thinnest haze, and it seemed to derive its whiteness as much from the virgin snow on the ground as from above. I could not cease to marvel at this light which seemed to be without a source—like the halo around the Saviour's face. The eye as yet did not reach very far, and wherever I looked, I found but one word to describe it: impalpable—and that is saying what it was not rather than what it was. As I said, there was no sunshine, but the light was there, omnipresent, diffused, coming mildly, softly, but from all sides, and out of all things as well as into them . . .

Oh, the surpassing beauty of it! There stood the trees, motionless under that veil of mist, and not their slenderest finger but was clothed in white. And the white it was! A translucent white, receding into itself, with strange backgrounds of white behind it—a modest white, and yet full of pride. An elusive white, and yet firm and substantial. The white of a diamond lying on snow-white velvet, the white of a diamond in diffused light. None of the sparkle and colour play that the most precious of stones assumes under a definite, limited light which proceeds from a definite, limited source. Its colour play was suggested, it is true, but so subdued that you hardly thought of naming or even recognizing its component parts. There was no red or yellow or blue or violet, but merely that which might flash into red and yellow and blue and violet, should perchance the sun break forth and monopolize the luminosity of the atmosphere. There was, as it were, a latent opalescence.

And every twig and every bough, every branch and every limb, every trunk and every crack even in the bark was furred with it. It seemed as if the hoarfrost still continued to form. It looked heavy, and yet it was nearly without weight. Not a twig was bent down under its load, yet with its halo of frost it measured fully two inches across. The crystals were large, formed like spearheads, flat, slablike, yet of infinite thinness and delicacy, so thin and light that, when by misadventure my whip touched the boughs, the flakes seemed to float down rather than to fall. And every one of these flat and angular slabs was fringed with hairlike needles, or with featherlike needles, and longer needles stood in between. There was such an air of fragility about it all that you hated to touch it—and I, for one, took my whip down lest it shook bare too many boughs . . .

On that short mile along the first of the east-west grades, before again I turned into the bush, I was for the thousandth time in my life struck with the fact how winter blots out the sins of utility. What is useful, is often ugly because in our fight for existence we do not always have the time or effort to spare to consider the looks of things. But the slightest cover of snow will bury the eyesores. Snow is the greatest equalizer in Nature. No longer are there fields and wild lands, beautiful trails and ugly grades—all are hidden away under that which comes from Nature's purest hands and fertile thoughts alone. Now there was no longer the raw, offending scar on Nature's body; just a smooth expanse of snow-white ribbon that led afar . . .

But then the turn into the bushy trail was reached. I did not see the slightest sign of it on the road. But Dan seemed infallible—he made the turn. And again I was in Winter's enchanted palace, again the slight whirl in the air that our motion set up made the fairy tracery of the boughs shower down upon me like snow-white petals of flowers, so delicate that to disturb the virginity of it all seemed like profaning the tempel of the All-Highest.

But then I noticed that I had not been the first one to visit the woods. All over their soft-napped carpet floor there were the restless, fleeting tracks of the snowflake, lacing and interlacing in lines and loops, as if they had been assembled in countless numbers, as no doubt they had. And every track looked like nothing so much as like that kind of embroidery, done white upon white, which ladies, I think, call the feather stitch. In places I could clearly see how they had chased and pursued each other, running, and there was a merriness about their spoors, a suggestion of swiftness which made me look up and about to see whether they were not wheeling their restless curves and circles overhead . . .

Meanwhile we were winging along ourselves, so it seemed. For there was the second east-west grade ahead. And that made me think of wife and child to whom I was coming like Santa Claus, and so I stopped under a bush that overhung the trail; and though I hated to destroy even a trifling part of the beauty around, I reached high up with my whip and let go at the branches, so that the moment before the horses bolted, the flakes showered down upon me and my robes and the cutter and changed me into a veritable snowman in snow-white garb . . .

They knew I was coming. They were at this very moment flying to meet me with their thoughts. Was I well? Was I finding everything as I had wished to find it? And though I often told them how I loved and enjoyed my drives, they could not view them but with much anxiety, for they were waiting, waiting, waiting . . .

And at last I swung west again, up the ridge and on to the yard. And there on the porch stood the tall, young, smiling woman, and at her knee the fairest-haired girl in all the world. And quite unconscious of Nature's wonder-garb, though doubtlessly gladdened by it, the little girl shrilled out, 'Oh, Daddy, Daddy, did du see Santa Claus?' And I replied lustily, 'Of course, my girl, I am coming straight from his palace.'

FREDERICK PHILIP GROVE

For the Yuletide Feast

To step inside there on a December day, half blinded by the dazzle of sun on snow, was to be Ali Baba entering the vast gloom of the treasure cave. For a moment I could see only dimly the laden shelves and counters. But even before my eyes had adjusted to the light my nostrils were aware of many odours—coffee, apples, warm bread, spices, tea and oranges, mingled with others pleasant but unidentifiable, in a symphonic smell of good food.

The food department of the Hudson's Bay Company's store was large, but it was not bright, obvious, and slickly hygienic as the big markets are now. It did not suggest a quick feed by fluorescent glare at an enamel-topped table in a corner of the kitchen, but rather, long feasts by candlelight at the knightly board. The dark wood in the long counters, in the high shelves lining the walls, in the ranks of cupboards and deep, mysterious bins, gave it a mellow, grand, baronial air . . . Here were barrels of apples, crates of oranges and tangerines, and brown Spanish casks full of grapes packed in crumbled cork: malagas as cool as jade, and great hothouse clusters that were deep purple beneath a frosty bloom.

Here, too, were the dried fruits, the raisins, currants, cherries, citron and angelica for the Christmas cakes and puddings. Mamma had bought her supply of these on an earlier expedition, and our Christmas cakes had been made. Everyone in the house had stirred a wish into them before they were put in the oven to bake for hours. Then, for two or three days they had stood on trays in the pantry while juice from preserved cherries and plums was poured over them and allowed to soak in. Finally they had been bathed in brandy and now, blanketed under an inch of almond paste, they were dozing boozily in the fruit cellar.

Today we would buy clusters of table raisins to nibble and almonds and walnuts to crack lazily at the end of dinner, when appetite had changed to a feeling of obesity, but the hand was still moving automatically to the mouth, *allargando*, like a metronome running down.

Here, too, we ordered our Christmas candies and it was hard to choose. There were bright marzipan fruits, *langues de chat* in flat boxes, silver-wrapped sweet chocolate tied with bright ribbons, yellow twists of barley sugar, butterscotch wafers and rum toffee. Dangling from a wire hung above the counter were the red-and-white peppermint canes for the Christmas tree, and small plum puddings looking like fat friars in their brown or white cloth sacks. In *Mother Goose* there was a rhyme about a king 'who stole three pecks of barley meal to make a bag pudding'. It must have been larger than these, for:

> The King and Queen did eat thereof,
> And all the court beside;
> And what they did not eat that night
> The Queen next morning fried.

Like mush, I supposed. It made the family life of ancient English royalty seem so cozy, and I longed to taste one of these little puddings. But mamma scorned them because they were boiled instead of steamed. For our own pudding she bought here a set of good luck charms: a ring, a thimble, a threepenny bit, a donkey and a four-leafed shamrock.

And then we came to the most festive and exciting of all these special, holiday things: the crackers. Some of them were magnificent, with gilt or silver trimming on the coloured crêpe paper. Some were decorated with artificial flowers or tinsel butterflies for the ladies to pin on their dresses or wear in their hair. But that was only the outside. A small label on the end of each box told what was inside the crackers: caps, charms, fake jewelry, conundrums, jokes or epigrams. Sometimes there were several prizes in each.

Oh, what delight—before the turkey was brought on—to find your cracker! What excitement to pull it with your neighbour, getting your fingers firmly on the snapper and making a terrific bang! And then the unwrapping, the unfolding of the paper caps that might be crowns or baby bonnets. And after the caps were put on, everyone read the joke or the riddle he had found. The epigrams were cribbed from Voltaire and Lord Chesterfield, and sometimes the riddles were pedantic. I remember one that sounded as if it had been made up by some waggish don: 'Why is a misogynist like an epithalamium?' But most were better suited to the varied ages of a Christmas family party. Merriment would dent two dimples high in my little cousin's cheeks as she read hers: 'Why does a sculptor die a horrible death?' 'Why?' we would all ask, and shout with laughter at the answer: 'Because he makes faces and busts!'

When we had chosen our box of crackers we came to the last stop, the department where the wines and liquors were sold. These shelves had a regimental look, with the bottles all in line, shoulder to shoulder, like soldiers on the parade ground. They were not, I thought, so beautiful as the shelves of jellies, for here dark glass often hid the colours of the wines. And my palate was too young to appreciate the contents. But as mamma ordered, the names took on an aura of festivity. First, claret for the holiday dinners. Even the children would have a few drops of claret in their glasses—enough to make the water a faint pink and to make us feel regal. Then brandy, to put around the pudding and set alight. And sherry, to serve to callers and to put in the grownups' pudding sauce. Children had lemon sauce, but at about twelve years it was possible to graduate to a small helping of the grown-ups' nectar, silky smooth with eggs, heavenly sweet with sugar, and divinely fiery with sherry.

RUTH HARVEY

The Concert

▲ ▲ ▲ ▲ ▲ ▲ ▲ ▲ ▲ ▲ ▲ ▲ ▲ ▲ ▲ ▲ ▲ ▲ ▲ ▲
● ● ● ● ● ● ● ● ● ● ● ● ● ● ● ● ● ● ● ●

The next night was the night of the concert. David's head felt light. The words of the play kept up an uncontrollable chatter in his mind. Supper made a taste in his mouth like the taste after running.

'Why won't you let us *hear* your piece, Dave?' his mother said.

He couldn't tell her why not. She wouldn't understand about the curtain and the spell. He felt as if his refusing was betrayal—but he could only speak the lines aloud *there*, or when he was by himself. Or with Effie and Anna.

He was saying them to himself as he poked hay in to the cows. He didn't hear his father's footsteps behind him.

'That sounds all right,' Joseph said.

But they sounded silly to David then. He stopped short. He tried to imitate his father's voice in the barn. 'Git yer head *back* there, you damn . . ." he shouted at the black cow.

As the time came closer still, the words touched his mind with the chill of bedclothes touching his flesh times he'd had a fever. His arms were trembling so when his mother made last-minute alterations in the sleeve lengths of his new suit that he could hardly hold them straight at his sides. He almost wished he'd refused to take a piece at all, like Chris had. Chris never had to do anything but *listen*.

A wire was stretched across the platform of the schoolhouse. Bed-sheets were looped over it for a curtain. Behind this curtain a small corner of the stage had been screened off for a dressing room. Here the teacher and the children were clotted.

The children whispered frenziedly. They fussed continuously with their costumes. They ran to the teacher with bright, terrible confidences: 'Miss Speakman, Tim can't find his star!' 'Miss Speakman, the oil's almost below the wick.' 'Miss Speakman, it looks like the curtain's caught—right there, see?'

Miss Speakman fixed the lamp and the curtain. She made Tim another tinsel star. She told Cora, through the pins in her mouth, for heaven's sake to keep her head still. She said, 'Danny, don't you dare to laugh tonight and spoil *everything*.'

Some of the children got out the scribbler pages their pieces were written on. The pages were worn furry at the creases. They read them over desperately, as if to catch the words before they rushed off the lines. Some whispered them out loud in a solemn voice. Some moved their lips and said them over only in their heads. Some of them peeked through the curtain.

The audience had straggled up the road with their lanterns, in groups of two and four, talking around the edge of things as they always did when they went together to something after dark. Now they were cramped awkwardly into the desk seats.

Once they had sat there as children themselves. They had had the thought ahead of no more school shiver in them like a different breath. But now they waited, patiently, for their own children to come out and say their pieces. These children seemed younger than they had ever been. They seemed older than these children would ever be.

The children peeked and giggled.

'I saw Mother, but she didn't see *me*.'

'Old Herb Hennessey's there!'

'Miss Speakman? I gotta go out!'

('Oh Lord! Well, slip out the side door. Now don't get snow on that crepe paper.')

'Miss Speakman, what time is it?'

'What time is it, Miss Speakman?'

'How much longer?'

('Oh, please be quiet. Why can't you act like David there? He isn't making a sound.')

He couldn't. He was absolutely still inside. The moment when he must say the first lines of the play had started to move toward him.

There was no comfort in anyone near. It was worse than being sick. Then the other faces were outside your pain, but when they smiled at you the pain softened. Now he was absolutely alone. Even Anna's smile was the smile of a photograph, a smile of some other time. The people outside the curtain seemed to have a cruel strangeness about them. He felt as if nakedness had spread his face and body wide and unmanageable. The words of the play were frozen. They had no feeling at all.

He tried to think of tomorrow. Somehow, tomorrow must come.

'Shhhhhhh . . .' The moment stopped moving. The curtain was pulled back.

'Ladies and gentlemen . . .'

David listened to Anna's opening recitation. She said her piece better than the others—almost as if it were something she'd thought up herself; only hesitant for trying to say it exactly the way he'd told her to . . .

The others said their pieces doggedly, as if they were reading the words off their mind. The spring of their nervousness kept jerking the words out one by one until the spring finally ran down. They said the funny parts in the dialogue as they read the words in a lesson they weren't quite sure how to pronounce. David wondered why the audience laughed. You could see they weren't speaking to each *other;* it was just the lines of the book talking back and forth. When they came back to the dressing room their excitement was only because it was over; not because for a minute they had made themselves into someone else.

The tableau came next. The teacher had planned this as a stunning surprise. The children had been pledged not to breathe a word of it beforehand.

Anna and Charlotte stood on two chairs. Effie stood, between and above them, on a step ladder. Everything was swathed first in sheets, then in billows of cheesecloth. The three figures were supposed to come out of a cloud. Their hair was combed out loose about their shoulders: Anna's a soft brown; Charlotte's coal black; and Effie's a light thin gold. Each had a silver crown—of stiff cardboard covered with pressed-out tea lead. Each had across her breast a wide band of flour bag dyed scarlet; with cut-out lettering so that a legend showed in white from the cheesecloth beneath.

Anna's was FAITH; Charlotte's HOPE; and Effie's LOVE.

'Now don't move,' the teacher whispered.

The audience was as immobile as the girls. It was like a spell. It was as if some beautiful flower that grew only in warm climates had suddenly sprung up in their own fields. They didn't see where the cheesecloth gaped behind the ladder, or the little cracks in Effie's crown where

the tea lead was joined or the tiny trembling of Anna's hand or
Charlotte's black shoes that she had seen before Christmas . . .

The teacher disentangled the cheesecloth both hastily and with
caution not to tear it. It would be cut up and distributed for table
throws. The older boys, Chris amongst them, came back to set up the
castle for the play.

The castle was a cardboard front; crenulated at the top like a geography castle, and nailed to uprights of two-by-four.

David wished desperately that he was Chris. Whatever Chris had to
do was always so simple. It was like lifting. The weight was there and
the muscles were there. You just put them together.

Effie was a princess, so she kept on her crown. She had a ruby neck-
lace of wild rosebush seed-sacs. She had a brooch of Ellen's at the neck
of her silk dress (though it had a real diamond, it didn't shine near so
brightly as the rhinestone brooch her mother had bought her in town),
and she wore a beaded and tasseled sash that Martha had come across
in the attic. Her slippers came from an old trunk of Ellen's. They were
too large, but they had high heels and were made not of leather but of
some brocaded material almost like dress stuff.

David wore only his plain corduroy suit at first. At the very end he'd
step behind the castle and come out in the crimson cape, with a piece
of snow-white rabbit fur sewn on the collar. They had copied it from a
picture of the little Plantagenets in his history book.

'And now, ladies and gentlemen . . .'

'Come on, Dave,' Anna said.

She took his hand, as if for a minute she were the older one because
it was he who must go. She could go no farther with him than the edge
of the curtain. David stepped out on the stage.

ERNEST BUCKLER

A Shopping Guide, 1876

★ ★

'Just at this season of the year the pertinent question is: What to purchase as a present?'

This was the question *The Gazette* asked in 1876, and it provided the answer. It printed a column, covering all persons and their Christmas needs.

The Gazette's shopping adviser believed that everyone must have some bachelor friend on his Christmas list. What should he buy him? Why, something from the tobacconist, of course. And why something from the tobacconist? Because smoking would relieve that loneliness which weighs so heavily upon the bachelor's mind. More than this, perchance he might see in the smoke rings visions of some better and happier life.

This shopping adviser of 1876 was convinced that of all things to drive away dull care and cheer a bachelor's sad heart, nothing can approach a good cigar, or a good pipe filled with good tobacco. For the bachelor, as a rule, works all day and sometimes far into the night, and finally retires into his chambers tired, feverish, and with a dull sense of his own nothingness. He lights a good cigar and puffs away silently for a few minutes.

The clouds of smoke ascend to the ceiling and carry with them the clouds from his brain. His face assumes a more cheerful expression, which gradually changes to an air of calm contemplation. Perhaps he sees a fair face beaming into his own, and he fondly thinks of the day, which the smoke seems to bring nearer, when he shall be a husband, with the owner of that face for a wife.

Such a gift to such a man might be the beginning of his true happiness. 'But for the cigar,' the shopping adviser pointed out, 'he would become a gloomy misanthrope, a burden to himself, and a nuisance to his acquaintances. Under such circumstances, who would not do anything to secure his happiness and wean him from his lonely life into the family circle? Surely, no one! Therefore, let all who have bachelor friends lose no time in visiting the smoking emporium.'

Having settled the bachelor friend, *The Gazette*'s shopping adviser passed on to the counterparts of the opposite sex. For these, he notices, 'cousins is the most convenient term and is very often used.'

Here the variety of appropriate gifts was certainly greater than for the melancholy bachelor. There were watches—those curious little bijoux. As for statues and clocks, the Montreal shops excelled, offering specimens 'which would grace the salons of St. Cloud or do honor to Windsor's honored halls.' There were ladies' work baskets, with well-stocked compartments beautifully lined with silk or satin, or with the best of woods.

There were also albums for collecting lines of poetry and autographs, their binding and gold designs being 'elegant beyond description'. There were photograph albums, and photographs visible when held up to the light—'a most desirable object at this season'. There was, certainly, no lack of gifts for such names as these on the Christmas list. Indeed, the stores were dazzling with suggestions.

Then, of course, on every married man's list would be the name of his wife. Here came suggestions to dignify the matron. The gift might be 'a new dress—a new shawl—an astrakan cloak—a silk dress of dark blue or seal brown'. Any such gifts would enhance and supplement the matron's established dignity.

Then there were the children—the most innocent merrymakers of the Christmas season. For them were candies. But *The Gazette* warned that these candies must be selected with wise care. Like medicine, they had to be given in doses adapted to the child's age. Candies for infants should be rigorously plain. For children of three and four years there might be candied almonds and chocolates. Those who had outgrown their pinafores might be given gum drops, lemon drops, crystallized fruits, or, perhaps, a cornucopia, filled with a variety of sweets.

There were also books for children—'all kinds of useful and orna-mental tales'. There were books of pictorial scenes of Jack-the-Giant-Killer, which led the three-year-old into the alphabet by a sort of kindergarten leading-string, which connected 'the young one's curios-ity with his knowledge in an improving way'. There was, too, the tale of 'the Robin and of the murderous sparrow who knocked him over'. And, of course, what child would not rejoice to receive a copy of *Pilgrim's Progress*?

Finally, for children there were the purses, or 'portmonies', which fond parents could purchase for their little ones, fill up with money, and give Santa Claus the credit.

For most other names on the Christmas list, *The Gazette*'s adviser recommended good eatables. Indeed, the Montreal shops were said to offer a spectacle of good things worthy of the display presented to Scrooge by the Spirit of Christmas Present. There were canned fruits from California; crystallized fruits from Paris; almonds from the Jordan; marmalades and jellies from all parts of Europe; Valencia, Muscatel and Sultana raisins; Scotch haggis, game, oysters, hams and bacons.

There were also, needless to say, all kinds of wines and liqueurs. In fact there were baskets of champagne, such as might be freely given even to the temperance men of *The Montreal Witness*. For these were only mimic presents of champagne, made of chocolate, put up in tiny baskets, and the exact counterfeit in shape of the ordinary champagne bottle. Such bottles were 'dry, very dry to the taste'. But to the temperance man, no doubt, they were a hundred per cent more agreeable.

But no shopping list of 1876 would be complete without its Christmas holly or mistletoe. At this point, indeed, *The Gazette*'s shopping adviser grew quite lyrical. 'Sing ho for the holly and the mistletoe,' he wrote, 'those emblems of joyfulness during the British Christmas holiday season, fraught with pleasant memories to those who have left the dear old land—memories that have been transmitted along with the bone and sinew of the good old stock to the citizens of our own Canada . . . Plum pudding and roast beef are always suggested by the mistletoe, and, in fact, everything that is substantial in Britain or British character comes trooping up in the panorama before our mind's eye as we look upon the holly and mistletoe.'

Last of all *The Gazette*'s adviser thought there was one name all too often omitted by the shopper, but which he might well include on his Christmas list. This was the name of the shopper himself. He thought that there was an admirable good sense in the Irishman who used to give presents 'to himself, from himself, for his own good conduct.'

At this point, however, *The Gazette*'s shopping adviser lost all the romance of Christmas and became no more than the depressingly prosaic Victorian. For he suggested that the Christmas shopper could do nothing better for himself than to purchase 'woollen underclothing, imported or domestic'.

EDGAR ANDREW COLLARD

A Victorian Innovation

Christmas for the Cartwrights a hundred years ago was rather a different affair from the hectic, somewhat overwhelming season of good cheer we know to-day. For Mamma and Papa there was no last-minute shopping, no gift-wrapping, no cards to be mailed. For the children, no bevy of Rudolphs, Sparkys and Frostys swarmed in their dreams. A blast like the one Canadian psychiatrist Brock Chisholm delivered against Santa Claus in 1945 was unthinkable in 1855—not only because Chisholm hadn't yet appeared on the scene but because Santa Claus hadn't appeared either. Indeed, Christmas, as we know it in Canada now, was only beginning to take shape.

To see what a Canadian Christmas was like a hundred years ago, let us spend the happy day of December 25, 1855, with the Cartwrights. They are an imaginary family, of course, but the individual members seem very real. There is Papa, a large and prosperous Toronto merchant who has chosen to live in that city both for business reasons and by the inclination of his Tory heart. There is mama, mild and capable, her tiny-waisted beauty that first caught Papa's eye lost to forty years of vast Victorian eating and a vast Victorian brood of eleven children. (In those days of high infant mortality it wasn't an unusual tragedy that six of them had died very young.)

There are Martha and Lucy, married daughters in their early thirties, who have come home for Christmas along with their husbands Joe and Charlie, and their children. Martha has three and Lucy four—little Marys and Jacks and Sophies, and Alma, the baby named for the allied victory at the River Alma in the Crimea the year before. Brother Frank Cartwright is home, too—in fact he has never left it. Still in his middle twenties but already a born bachelor, he is stout, rosy-cheeked, amiable and self-sufficient. The older brothers, George and Henry, who are married, live too far away to journey home for the holiday. There will be many more Cartwright family connections at Christmas dinner itself—Uncle Tom and Uncle Herbert from Mamma's family and Uncle Richard from Papa's, the maiden aunts Lucy, Emily and

Charlotte and an assortment of cousins. Altogether there will be nearly thirty, all looking forward to what a Toronto newspaper of the period spoke of as 'the new German way of celebrating Christmas'. What the paper didn't mention was that the new German way had spread to Canada from England, where it had been introduced by the Prince Consort and made fashionable by his pretty young Queen. And no Canadians were quicker to follow Victoria's royal example than people like the Cartwrights, solidly prosperous Anglicans (the other Protestant faiths were slower to recognize Christmas as a combined sacred and secular festival).

The Cartwrights slept well that Christmas Eve. Unlike their descendants today, they hadn't exhausted themselves with long-drawn-out preparations for the morrow or by a rush of last-minute shopping. They had obtained their Christmas tree, the chief feature of the new way of celebrating, by the simple expedient of telling their manservant to go out to the woods at the edge of the city and cut one. And since presents were only sent to one's very best friends and immediate relatives, they hadn't been much of a problem.

Nor had the Cartwrights sat up late addressing uncountable Christmas cards to almost total strangers. It would be another fifteen years or so before the custom of sending cards caught on to any extent, and about ten years before the now classic figure of Santa Claus appeared. That benign gentleman was first pictured, by a supreme stroke of irony, by the American political cartoonist, Thomas Nast, whose savage caricatures of Boss Tweed did so much to ruin that crooked pillar of New York's Tammany Hall. The nearest equivalents of Santa on the rare Christmas cards of 1855 were tiny gnomelike creatures with pointed ears, or stately bishops, or severe-looking pagan druids. And the first Christmas card of all, designed by an English painter named Horsley for what he called 'Xmasse 1843' was a drawing of a family at their traditionally huge Victorian Christmas dinner.

For the Cartwrights there were to be four kinds of soup: oyster (the oysters were dried and shipped from the Atlantic coast in small wooden casks), chicken, gumbo and mutton broth. Mamma had arranged for four boiled dishes: beef, pork, mutton and, of all things, boiled turkey served with a sauce of melted butter. There wasn't much choice of vegetables, but she'd provided for steaming mountains of potatoes, carrots, turnips and onions. For the main course there were no fewer than seven different roasts—beef, pork, mutton and turkey again, together with venison, chickens and geese . . .

On Christmas morning, the kitchen staff began work at dawn. Meanwhile Papa and Mamma and the family were waked at their usual hour of eight to dress for the great day . . .

Right after breakfast (lamb chops, deviled kidneys and great bowls of porridge) came the official recognition of the Christmas tree, which had been set up in the drawing room by the manservant, and trimmed by the maid under the direction of Mamma. Since the idea of having one was still such a novelty, she'd had to go by the account of Queen Victoria's tree at Windsor Castle in the *Illustrated London News*:

'The tree employed for this festive purpose is a young fir about eight feet high, and has six tiers of branches. Pendent from the branches are elegant trays, baskets, *bonbonnières,* and other receptacles for sweetmeats. Fancy cakes, gilt gingerbread and eggs filled with sweetmeats are also suspended by variously colored ribbons from the branches. The tree, which stands upon a table covered with white damask, is supported at the root by piles of sweets of a larger kind and by toys and dolls.'

Mamma Cartwright wasn't able to match the superlative elegance of the royal tree, but she managed to please Papa and enthrall the children all the same. For the sweetmeats there were lozenges, both plain and with little mottoes written on them, and an astonishing variety of fruit drops—strawberry, grape, apple, pear, raspberry and lemon, each in the shape of the respective fruit. There were china baskets filled with sugared almonds, and bundles of licorice sticks, together with shining rings of colored barley sugar which looked like jeweled bracelets.

The presents at the foot of the tree, as at Windsor, were mostly toys. There were dolls of wax, the most coveted; of china, considered second-best; and of papier-mâché, not so popular but guaranteed unbreakable. There were hobby-horses, rocking horses, and miniature violins and guitars made of painted tin and thoughtfully designed to produce almost no sound. And because this was Canada, there were little ice skates with upcurling runners for the children, as well as wooden sleighs and toboggans.

The toys were nearly always bought but some of the presents the grownups got had been made at home. Their store-bought gifts ran heavily to coral and jet brooches and cameos for the women, and studs, sleeve links and scarfpins for the men. The home-made gifts were more original, and some were positively grotesque. Painted perfume bottles weren't so bad, being ornamented with winter scenes in which the snow was glittering diamond dust sprinkled on fish glue. But there were also things like the 'useful gift to a young man' described in a how-to-do-it newspaper piece. It was what was called a laundry-pincushion:

'On the left-hand side of a cushion six inches long, made of soft silk of apple-green hue, there is a narrow strip of celluloid, upon which are written in Roman letters names of the usual articles sent to the laundry. Then lines are neatly drawn across the cushion and long-itudinally also. At the top of the cushion are the figures from one to nine. Now if there were fifteen handkerchiefs sent to the laundry, a pin will be stuck in opposite the word on the left and in the little square under the figures eight and seven.'

When the tree had been admired and the presents distributed (it wasn't the custom to wrap them unless they were intended to be surprises), the whole family set off for church, trudging decorously along the snow-covered plank side-walks of those calm times.

Since their ears hadn't been assaulted for the past four weeks by Christmas carols roaring metallically out of amplifiers everywhere, they greatly enjoyed the singing. *While Shepherds Watched Their Flocks By Night,* which had been newly set to music in 1850, was just begin-ning to become a familiar part of Christmas, but that year of 1855 the Cartwrights heard for the first time what is now perhaps the most famous Christmas hymn of all. The words had been written by Charles Wesley, brother of the founder of Methodism, and the music was adapted from Mendelssohn's *Festgesang* by a man named Cummings earlier in 1855. The name of it was *Hark, the Herald Angels Sing.*

After church, the family went home to the enormous dinner that awaited them. And after dinner, when the wonderful fullness had worn off enough to allow everyone to move about without gasping, there were the children's games . . .

JAMES BANNERMAN

An Evening with Dickens in Manitou Town Hall

Mr. Vander was 'a meek little man with a Byronic face who spoke beautiful English and read from the classics'. His wife 'went out working by the day, a tired draggled woman, who accepted her lot in life without complaint'.

He tried teaching in a country school, but soon gave up because he could not 'reach' the people in the district. His neighbors remonstrated with him:

'Mr. Vander,' I went on, 'you should try to grow up and assume some responsibility. You left that school because you wanted to come back to that easy chair where food and lodging are provided by your wife's efforts. Have you no pride?'

'Pride!' He caught at the word eagerly. 'Yes, madam, I have pride. I have pride of ancestry, nationality and tradition. I am proud of my heritage of English literature and if you and my wife will refrain from interrupting me I will take you into my confidence. I have a plan to help my fellow men, an infinitely better plan than this teaching scheme, one into which I can put my whole heart.'

He was off on his magic carpet, leaving the cares of the world behind him, and strangely enough he was able to make us listen.

His plan was, in brief, to give readings from Dickens' *Christmas Carol* two days before Christmas. He would make his own tickets and send the children out to sell them:

AN EVENING WITH DICKENS—THE CHRISTMAS CAROL

Interpreted by Frederick T. Vander,

late of Drury Lane, London

Manitou Town Hall

Admission by Ticket Only

That cold December night came down in the best Manitoba tradition, a windy night, with stars hanging low in a sky of cold steel. A cold night never held any of us in if we wanted to go out so the McClung family was represented by three members—Jack, Florence and myself.

The hall was a draughty place, heated by one stove in the middle of the room. A straggling audience occupied the zone around the stove and a fair pile of firewood promised a continuance of heat. (The newspaper said in its account of the gathering that 'the intelligence of the audience made up for the smallness of its numbers'.)

Promptly at eight o'clock the Interpreter, Mr. Frederick T. Vander, in evening dress, came out from the back room with a copy of the *Christmas Carol* in his hand. He was in good voice and looked like a perfect Bob Cratchit. He even had the white scarf inside his coat with its fluttering white ends. I resolutely put aside the opinion I had of him as a husband and father and settled down to enjoy the performance.

'Marley was dead,' he began, and we were off. Let the wind blow, let the tin roof crackle and buckle, we were listening to an immortal tale. The little man knew how to present his story. He played all parts with equal facility; he was Scrooge, tight-fisted and wizened, harsh of voice and hard of heart; he was the timid little clerk trying to warm himself at the candle. He was the fog that came pouring into every chink, 'making the houses across the street into mere phantoms'. And how well he did the nephew all in a glow of good fellowship who came in to wish old Scrooge a merry Christmas!—which he defined as—'A kind forgiving charitable time . . . when men and women open their shut-up hearts freely and think of the people below them as fellow passengers to the grave, and not another race bound on other journeys'!

So intent were we on the story that no one noticed that the fire was burning low and it was not until the knocker on the door changed to Marley's face that someone on the outer fringe of the audience came forward and mended the fire noisily. The Interpreter glared at the interruption but resumed the story. The caretaker of the hall, Mr. Miller, roused to his duty by this alien hand laid on his stove, reasserted his authority by piling in more wood and more wood, and soon the crackling of the stove joined the rumbling of the tin roof. The audience stretched their chilly hands to the warmth and went adventuring on the high seas where grizzled men raised their voices in praise of Christmas.

It was not until the Second Spirit entered that we began to feel sudden draughts across the floor as certain members of the audience drifted out. Each time the door opened a blast from the Arctic Circle smote us. Then, by sign language, we urged Mr. Miller to greater efforts.

About ten o'clock when Scrooge and the Spirit of Christmas Present went through the streets and saw 'The brightness of the roaring fires in kitchens where preparations for the Christmas dinner were going on and tantalizing smells of turkey and sage came through the doors as happy children ran out to meet their cousins arriving'—it was then I missed my firstborn who had noiselessly departed, but Florence stayed on. She was drawn as far into her coat as she could get and had gathered her feet under her for warmth.

We lost another detachment when the Crachits sat down to the goose, and the young Crachits crammed spoons into their mouths lest they should shriek for goose before their turn came to be helped.

By the time the last Spirit had taken Scrooge to see his grisly ending, the wind had risen to new heights, and not only the tin roof, but the timbers of the hall creaked and groaned, and made strange and threatening noises. The audience were all around the stove now and the Speaker was with us too. He had put on his overcoat and mittens.

We looked in vain for Mr. Miller, but it appeared that he had gone, and evidently had taken the last of the firewood with him, so there we were at the end of our resources, but not the end of the story.

We saw it out; we stayed until the end, which came about eleven; and in spite of the cold and the burned out fire, the crackling roof and the bitter wind that found out every crack in the old Orange Hall, in spite of everything, we felt the thrill of the awakened soul of Ebenezer Scrooge, as the magic of Christmas ran in our veins, setting at naught the discomfort of the hour.

Since then, many many times we have heard the story told in the golden voices of John and Lionel Barrymore, heard it in warm rooms brightened by wood fires, with plates of apples waiting for us, and the fragrance of coffee on the air. But it was on that cold night in the old Orange Hall in Manitou that Florence and I, numb to the knees, really entered into the magic circle of the Dickens' Fellowship, and we felt ever since that we have the right to gather with the faithful wherever they are.

NELLIE McCLUNG

Hoodoo McFiggin's Christmas

This Santa Claus business is played out. It's a sneaking, underhand method, and the sooner it's exposed the better.

For a parent to get up under cover of the darkness and palm off a ten-cent necktie on a boy who had been expecting a ten-dollar watch, and then say that an angel sent it to him, is low; undeniably low.

I had the good opportunity of observing how the thing worked this Christmas, in the case of young Hoodoo McFiggin, the son and heir of the McFiggins at whose house I board.

Hoodoo McFiggin is a good boy—a religious boy. He had been given to understand that Santa Claus would bring nothing to his father and mother because grown-up people don't get presents from the angels. So he saved up all his pocket money and bought a box of cigars for his father and a seventy-five cent diamond brooch for his mother. His own fortunes he left in the hands of the angels. But he prayed. He prayed every night for weeks that Santa Claus would bring him a pair of skates and a puppy dog and an air gun and a bicycle and a Noah's ark and a sleigh and a drum—altogether about a hundred and fifty dollars' worth of stuff.

I went into Hoodoo's room quite early Christmas morning. I had an idea that the scene would be interesting. I woke him up and he sat up in bed, his eyes glistening with radiant expectation, and began hauling things out of his stocking.

The first parcel was bulky; it was done up quite loosely and had an odd look generally.

'Ha! ha!' Hoodoo cried gleefully, as he began undoing it. 'I'll bet it's the puppy dog, all wrapped up in paper!'

And was it the puppy dog? No, by no means. It was a pair of nice, strong, number four boots, laces and all, labelled, 'Hoodoo, from Santa Claus,' and underneath Santa Claus had written, '.95 net'.

The boy's jaw fell with delight. 'It's boots,' he said, and plunged in his hand again.

He began hauling away at another parcel with renewed hope on his face.

This time the thing seemed like a little round box. Hoodoo tore the paper off it with a feverish hand. He shook it; something rattled inside.

'It's a watch and chain! It's a watch and chain!' he shouted. Then he pulled the lid off.

And was it a watch and chain? No. It was a box of nice, brand new celluloid collars, a dozen of them all alike and all his own size.

The boy was so pleased that you could see his face crack up with pleasure.

He waited a few minutes until his intense joy subsided. Then he tried again.

This time the packet was long and hard. It resisted the touch and had a sort of funnel shape.

'It's a toy pistol!' said the boy, trembling with excitement. 'Gee! I hope there are lots of caps with it! I'll fire some off now and wake up father.'

No, my poor child, you will not wake your father with that. It is a useful thing, but it needs no caps and it fires no bullets, and you cannot wake a sleeping man with a tooth brush. Yes, it was a tooth brush—a regular beauty, pure bone all through, and ticketed with a little paper, 'Hoodoo, from Santa Claus.'

Again the expression of intense joy passed over the boy's face, and the tears of gratitude started from his eyes. He wiped them away with his tooth brush and passed on.

The next packet was much larger and evidently contained something soft and bulky. It had been too long to go into the stocking and was tied outside.

'I wonder what this is,' Hoodoo mused, half afraid to open it. Then his heart gave a great leap, and he forgot all his other presents in the anticipation of this one. 'It's a drum!' he gasped. 'It's the drum, all wrapped up!'

Drum nothing! It was pants, a pair of the nicest little short pants—yellowish brown short pants—with dear little strips of colour running across both ways, and here again Santa Clause had written, 'Hoodoo, from Santa Claus, one forty net.'

But there was something wrapped up in it. Oh, yes! There was a pair of braces wrapped up in it, braces with a little steel sliding thing so that you could slide your pants up to your neck, if you wanted to.

The boy gave a dry sob of satisfaction. Then he took out his last present. 'It's a book,' he said, as he unwrapped it. 'I wonder if it is fairy stories or adventures. Oh, I hope it's adventures! I'll read it all morning.'

No, Hoodoo, it was not precisely adventures. It was a small family Bible. Hoodoo had now seen all his presents, and he arose and dressed. But he still had the fun of playing with his toys. That is always the chief delight of Christmas morning.

First he played with his tooth brush. He got a whole lot of water and brushed all his teeth with it. This was huge.

Then he played with his collars. He had no end of fun with them, taking them all out one by one and swearing at them, and then putting them back and swearing at the whole lot together.

The next toy was his pants. He had immense fun there, putting them on and taking them off again, and then trying to guess which side was which by merely looking at them.

After that he took his book and read some adventures called *Genesis* till breakfast time.

Then he went downstairs and kissed his father and mother. His father was smoking a cigar, and his mother had her new brooch on. Hoodoo's face was thoughtful, and a light seemed to have broken in upon his mind. Indeed, I think it altogether likely that next Christmas he will hang onto his own money and take chances on what the angels bring.

STEPHEN LEACOCK

Yuletide Sport

▲ ▲ ▲ ▲ ▲ ▲ ▲ ▲ ▲ ▲ ▲ ▲ ▲ ▲ ▲ ▲ ▲ ▲ ▲ ▲

Heavy snowfall in early December caused me to make inquiries regarding Christmas observance from some of the elderly people who have active memories, some folk lore of the days just before Confederation.

'We had very little in those days,' one veteran told me. 'Roads were of the most primitive sort. Corduroy helped us out. For the rest of the way we muddled through or went 'round swamps and bogs. When winter came, the snow blotted out everything in that line. We made our own snowshoes and got along as best we could.

'Of course we little fellows looked for Santa. Reindeer were real to us. We had sleighs that looked like his. Our presents consisted of things molded from maple sugar or wonderful delicacies, as we regarded them, made from such flour as we managed to get for the time. Of course there were new mitts and scarfs and mufflers and stockings manufactured at home, after being dyed from various barks mother knew about. Who cared if they turned all manner of colours before the winter was out! The specialty for dinner was pudding made from corn meal with the annual handful of raisins as never-to-be-forgotten delicacy.

'After dinner, we gave ourselves to sports. We'd gather at the post office and blacksmith shop for our yearly contests. There was the contest with the good old diamond-toothed crosscut saw. A maple log three feet through was selected and after careful measurement the contestants were at it. When four pairs of contestants were going their strongest, you had a sight you'd not forget. The dropping of the log was the signal for victory, an event heralded by a cheer that made the woods echo again. There was, too, the contest of putting up cordwood. Usually four would enter.

'Along with the axe went contests with rifle and gun. Indeed, it was doubtful which ranked the higher, the axeman or the man expert with gun or rifle. There were no breechloaders in those days. We had some of the old Queen Anne muskets, desperate weapons for the destruction they wrought and dreadful in their recoil. Many a good man has been sent sprawling as these weapons delivered their deadly 'kick'. All the year through we prepared our rifles and our guns for the great day. We knew to a grain how much the gun would explode by measuring the uncombusted powder that fell upon white paper placed under the gun as it was discharged. We knew just how tightly the powder and the shot charges should be impacted by the ramrod. We knew a good deal about lead from a rifleman's point of view and knew just how tightly the ball should fit, when it should be greased and when it should be driven home, covered with the well-greased rag.

'We knew, too, the degree of heat at which a rifle did its best. Of course we had no fine instruments for this purpose, but hardwon experience had taught us a good deal. We soon learned that we couldn't overlook anything when handling a rifle or axe.

'Last of all, we had the wrestling contests. The winner must prove the two out of three in collar and elbow, sideholds and catch-at-as-catch-can. This was a contest that required not only brawn, but endurance and self-control. No one could enter this contest who had not done well at the sawing or the woodcutting.

'Christmas was a great day with us. The victors of those days are for the most part forgotten, but they were heroes to us.'

JAMES ANTHONY

King for a Meal

★ ★ ★ ★ ★ ★ ★ ★ ★ ★ ★ ★ ★ ★ ★ ★ ★ ★ ★ ★

The following letter, received from Mr. S. E. Clement, of Brandon, was written by Mr. H. F. Maley, a former resident of that city, and presents a quaint and interesting sidelight on Christmas.

With reference to my representing His Majesty, the late King George V at a Christmas dinner in Moose Jaw.

At the time I was looking after a business for the Merchants Bank and we had a bookkeeper, an Englishman named John Spight.

Mr. Spight came to me the day before Christmas and asked me if I would have dinner with him on Christmas and that I should represent His Majesty, the King. I asked for some particulars and he told me the following story:

During the reign of King George III, Mr. Spight's ancestor lived on a small farm on the highway between London and Brighton. On Christmas Eve a party of gentlemen were returning to London from Brighton. They were late and about one o'clock in the morning the coach broke down in front of the little farm house where Mr. Spight lived. The night was cold and the coach party woke up the people of the house and asked to be taken in while the coach was undergoing repairs. (The party had a wheelwright with them to look after the coach.)

The Spight family got up, took them in, entertained them to a fine dinner which they had prepared for their own Christmas and all had a pleasant time. When the coach was repaired and the travellers prepared to leave, the leading gentleman of the party thanked their host for his kindness in taking them in and for the splendid repast they had all enjoyed and he asked him if there were anything he could do for him as he had some influence. In reply Mr. Spight said he did not know of anything in particular that he wanted unless it was the twenty acre field on the opposite side of the road. The party then resumed their journey.

Mr. Spight did not hear anything further on the matter, in fact, had forgotten about it when one day a Courier arrived from London who delivered to him a title for the twenty acres of land. The title stated that the property in question should be the property of Mr. Spight, his heirs and assigns as long as the sun shone and water ran down hill. The only provision in the deal was that on Christmas day he, or the owner of the property should provide the best dinner procurable either at home or at the best tavern or hotel in the place where he resided at the time and that the King must be invited; in the event of the King being unable to attend, the owner of the property should appoint some person to represent the King and that the receipt should be taken from the Hotel proprietor or clerk and signed by Mr. Spight and whoever represented the King. We dined at Harry Meads Hotel, it being the leading one in Moose Jaw at that time. The receipt was duly executed as required and forwarded to a firm of solicitors residing in Innfield Lane in London, England.

I asked Spight if he ever knew of any of the dinners being attended by the King. He said, 'Yes,' that King Edward VII had attended one given by Spight's father.

King Edward VII was a trap shooter and Spight's father was also and they were shooting at a Tournament at Cannes in France. While in conversation with King Edward, Mr. Spight told him about the property and the condition under which it was held and asked him to attend one of the dinners. The King agreed and set the time for dinner and said he regretted that he would have to leave immediately after the dinner as he had many social obligations on Christmas day. The King attended the dinner.

WINNIPEG FREE PRESS

An Orange from Portugal

I suppose all of us, when we think of Christmas, recall Charles Dickens and our own childhood. So, today, from an apartment in Montreal, looking across the street to a new neon sign, I think back to Dickens and Halifax and the world suddenly becomes smaller, shabbier and more comfortable, and one more proof is registered that comfort is a state of mind, having little to do with the number of springs hidden inside your mattress or the upholstery in your car.

Charles Dickens should have lived in Halifax. If he had, that brown old town would have acquired a better reputation in Canada than it now enjoys, for all over the world people would have known what it was like. Halifax, especially a generation or two ago, was a town Dickens could have used.

There were dingy basement kitchens all over the town where rats were caught every day. The streets were full of teamsters, hard-looking men with lean jaws, most of them, and at the entrance to the old North Street station cab drivers in long coats would mass behind a heavy anchor chain and terrify travellers with bloodcurdling howls as they bid for fares. Whenever there was a southeast wind, harbor bells moaned behind the wall of fog that cut the town off from the rest of the world. Queer faces peered at you suddenly from doorways set flush with the streets. When a regiment held a smoker in the old Masonic Hall you could see a line beginning to form in the early morning, waiting for the big moment at midnight when the doors would be thrown open to the town and any man could get a free drink who could reach the hogsheads.

For all these things Dickens would have loved Halifax, even for the pompous importers who stalked to church on Sunday mornings, swinging their canes and complaining that they never had a chance to hear a decent sermon. He would have loved it for the waifs and strays and beachcombers and discharged soldiers and sailors whom the respectable never seemed to notice, for all the numerous aspects of the town that made Halifax deplorable and marvelous.

If Dickens had been given a choice of a Canadian town in which to spend Christmas, that's where I think he would have gone, for his most obvious attitude toward Christmas was that it was necessary. Dickens was no scientist or organizer. Instead of liking The People, he simply liked people. And so inevitably, he liked places where accidents were apt to happen. In Halifax accidents were happening all the time. Think of the way he writes about Christmas—a perfect Christmas for him was always a chapter of preposterous accidents. Now, I don't think he would have chosen to spend his Christmas in Westmount or Toronto, for he'd be fairly sure that neither of those places needed it.

Today we know too much. Having become democratic by ideology, we are divided into groups which eye each other like dull strangers at a dull party, polite in public and nasty when each other's backs are turned. Today we are informed by those who know that if we tell children about Santa Claus we will probably turn them into neurotics. Today we believe in universal justice and in universal war to effect it, and because Santa Claus gives the rich more than he gives the poor, lots of us think it better that there should be no Santa Claus at all. Today we are technicians, and the more progressive among us see no reason why love and hope should not be organized in a department of the government, planned by a politician and administered by trained specialists. Today we have a supercolossal Santa Claus for The Customer: he sits in the window of department stores in a cheap red suit, stringy whiskers and a mask which is a caricature of a face, and for a month before every Christmas he laughs continually with a vulgar roar. The sounds of his laughter come from a record played over and over, and the machine in his belly that produces the bodily contortions has a number in the patent office in Washington.

In the old days in Halifax we never thought about the meaning of the word democracy; we were all mixed up together in a general deplorability. So the only service any picture of those days can render is to help prove how far we have advanced since then. The first story I have to tell has no importance and not even much of a point. It is simply the record of how one boy felt during a Christmas that now seems remote enough to belong to the era of Bob Cratchit. The second story is about the same. The war Christmases I remember in Halifax were not jolly ones. In a way they were half-tragic, but there may be some significance in the fact that they are literally the only ones I can still remember. Indirectly, the war was part of them both. It was a war nobody down there understood. We were simply a part of it, swept into it from the mid-Victorian Age in which we were all living until 1914.

On Christmas Eve in 1915 a cold northeaster was blowing through the town with the smell of coming snow on the wind. All day our house was hushed for a reason I didn't understand, and I remember being sent out to play with some other boys in the middle of the afternoon. Supper was a silent meal. And then, immediately after we had finished, my father put on the greatcoat of his new uniform and went to the door and I saw the long tails of the coat blowing out behind him in the flicker of a faulty arc light as he half-ran up to the corner.

We heard bagpipes, and almost immediately a company of soldiers appeared swinging down Spring Garden Road from old Dalhousie. It was very cold as we struggled up to the corner after my father, and he affected not to notice us. Then the pipes went by playing *The Blue Bonnets,* the lines of khaki men went past in the darkness and my father fell in behind the last rank and faded off down the half-lit street, holding his head low against the wind to keep his flat military cap from blowing off, and my mother tried to hide her feelings by saying what a shame the cap didn't fit him properly. She told my sister and me how nice it was of the pipers to have turned out on such a cold day to see the men off, for pipe music was the only kind my father liked. It was all very informal. The men of that unit—almost entirely a local one—simply left their homes the way my father had done and joined the column and the column marched down Spring Garden Road to the ship along the familiar route most of them had taken to church all their lives.

An hour later we heard tugboat whistles and then the foghorn of the transport and we knew he was on his way. As my sister and I hung up our stockings on the mantelpiece I wondered whether the vessel was no farther out than Thrum Cap or whether it had already reached Sambro.

It was a bleak night for children to hang up their stockings and wait for Santa Claus, but next morning we found gifts in them as usual, including a golden orange in each toe. It was strange to think that the very night my father had left the house, a strange old man, remembering my sister and me, had come into it. We thought it was a sign of good luck.

That was 1915, and sometime during the following year a boy at school told me there was no Santa Claus and put his case so convincingly that I believed him.

Strictly speaking, this should have been the moment of my first step toward becoming a neurotic. Maybe it was, but there were so many other circumstances to compete with it, I don't know whether Santa Claus was responsible for what I'm like now or not. For about a week after discovering the great deception I wondered how I could develop a line of conduct that would prevent my mother from finding out that I knew who filled our stockings on Christmas Eve. I hated to disappoint her in what I knew was a great pleasure. After a while I forgot all about it. Then, shortly before Christmas a cable arrived saying that my father was on his way home. He hadn't been killed like the fathers of other boys at school; he was being invalided home as a result of excessive work as a surgeon in the hospital.

We had been living with my grandmother in Cape Breton, so my mother rented a house in Halifax sight unseen; we got down there in time to meet his ship when it came in, and then we all went to the new house. This is the part of my story that reminds me of Charles Dickens again. Five minutes after we entered the house it blew up. This was not the famous Halifax explosion; we had to wait another year for that. This was our own private explosion. It smashed half the windows in the other houses along the block; it shook the ground like an earthquake and it was heard for a mile.

I have seen many queer accidents in Halifax, but none that gave the reporters more satisfaction than ours did. For a house to blow up suddenly in our district was unusual, so the press felt some explanation was due the public. Besides, it was nearly Christmas and local news was hard to find. The moment the first telephone call reached the newspaper offices to report the accident, they knew the cause. Gas had been leaking in our district for years and a few people had even complained about it. In our house, gas had apparently backed in from the city mains, filling partitions between the walls and lying stagnant in the basement. But this was the first time anyone could prove that gas had been leaking. The afternoon paper gave the story:

DOCTOR HUNTS GAS LEAK WITH BURNING MATCH—FINDS IT!

When my father was able to talk, which he couldn't do for several days because the skin had been burned off his hands and face, he denied the story about the match. According to modern theory this denial should have precipitated my second plunge toward neurosis, for I had distinctly seen him with the match in his hand, going down to the basement to look for the gas and complaining about how careless people were. However, those were ignorant times and I didn't realize I might get a neurosis. Instead of brooding and deciding to close my mind to reality from then on to preserve my belief in the veracity and faultlessness of my father, I wished to God he had been able to tell his story sooner and stick to it. After all, he was a first-class doctor, but what would prospective patients think if every time they heard his name they saw a picture of an absent-minded veteran looking for a gas leak in a dark basement with a lighted match?

It took two whole days for the newspaper account of our accident to settle. In the meantime the house was temporarily ruined, school children had denuded the chandelier in the living room of its prisms, and it was almost Christmas. My sister was still away at school, so my mother, my father and I found ourselves in a single room in an old residential hotel on Barrington Street. I slept on a cot and they nursed their burns in a huge bed which opened out of the wall. The bed had a mirror on the bottom of it, and it was equipped with such a strong spring that it crashed into place in the wall whenever they got out of it. I still remember my father sitting up in it with one arm in a sling from the war, and his face and head in white bandages. He was philosophical about the situation, including the vagaries of the bed, for it was his Calvinistic way to permit himself to be comfortable only when things were going badly.

The hotel was crowded and our meals were brought to us by a boy called Chester, who lived in the basement near the kitchen. That was all I knew about Chester at first; he brought our meals, he went to school only occasionally, and his mother was ill in the basement. But as long as my memory lasts, that Christmas of 1916 will be Chester's Christmas.

He was a waif of a boy. I never knew his last name, and wherever he is now, I'm certain he doesn't remember me. But for a time I can say without being sentimental that I loved him.

He was white-faced and thin, with lank hair on top of a head that broke back at right angles from a high narrow forehead. There were always holes in his black stockings, his handed-down pants were so badly cut that one leg was several inches longer than the other and there was a patch on the right seat of a different color from the rest of the cloth. But he was proud of his clothes; prouder than anyone I've ever seen over a pair of pants. He explained that they were his father's and his father had worn them at sea.

For Chester, nobody was worth considering seriously unless he was a seaman. Instead of feeling envious of the people who lived upstairs in the hotel, he seemed to feel sorry for them because they never went to sea. He would look at the old ladies with the kind of eyes that Dickens discovered in children's faces in London: huge eyes as trusting as a bird-dog's, but old, as though they had forgotten how to cry long ago.

I wondered at lot about Chester—what kind of a room they had in the basement, where they ate, what his mother was like. But I was never allowed in the basement. Once I walked behind the hotel to see if I could look through the windows, but they were only six or eight inches above the ground and they were covered with snow. I gathered that Chester liked it down there because it was warm, and once he was down nobody ever bothered him.

The days went past, heavy and grey and cold. Soon it was the day before Christmas again, and I was still supposed to believe in Santa Claus. I found myself confronted by a double crisis.

I would have to hang up my stocking as usual, but how could my parents, who were still in bed, manage to fill it? And how would they feel when the next morning came and my stocking was still empty? This worry was overshadowed only by my concern for Chester.

On the afternoon of Christmas Eve he informed me that this year, for the first time in his life, Santa Claus was really going to remember him. 'I never ett a real orange and you never did neether because you only get real oranges in Portugal. My old man says so. But Santy Claus is going to bring me one this year. That means the old man's still alive.'

'Honest, Chester? How do you know?' Everyone in the hotel knew that his father, who was a quartermaster, was on a slow convoy to England.

'Mrs. Urquhart says so.'

Everyone in the hotel also knew Mrs. Urquhart. She was a tiny old lady with a harsh voice who lived in the room opposite ours on the ground floor with her unmarried sister. Mrs. Urquhart wore a white lace cap and carried a cane. Both old ladies wore mourning—Mrs. Urquhart for two dead husbands, her sister for Queen Victoria. They were a trial to Chester because he had to carry hot tea upstairs for them every morning at seven.

'Mrs. Urquhart says if Santy Claus brings me real oranges it means he was talkin' to the old man and the old man told him I wanted one. And if Santy Claus was talkin' to the old man, it means the old man's alive, don't it?'

Much of this was beyond me until Chester explained further.

'Last time the old man was home I see'd some oranges in a store window, but he wouldn't get me one because if he buys stuff in stores he can't go on being a seaman. To be a seaman you got to wash out your insides with rum every day and rum costs lots of money. Anyhow, store oranges ain't real.'

'How do you know they aren't?'

'My old man says so. He's been in Portugal and he picks real ones off trees. That's where they come from. Not from stores. Only my old man and the people who live in Portugal has ever ett real oranges.'

Someone called and Chester disappeared into the basement. An hour or so later, after we had eaten the supper he brought to us on a tray, my father told me to bring the wallet from the pocket of his uniform, which was hanging in the cupboard. He gave me some small change and sent me to buy grapes for my mother at a corner fruit store. When I came back with the grapes I met Chester in the outer hall. His face was beaming and he was carrying a parcel wrapped in brown paper.

'Your old man give me a two-dollar bill,' he said. 'I got my old lady a Christmas present.'

I asked him if it was medicine.

'She don't like medicine,' he said. 'When she's feelin' bad she wants rum.'

When I got back to our room I didn't tell my father what Chester had done with his two dollars. I hung up my stocking on the old-fashioned mantelpiece, the lights were put out and I was told to go to sleep.

An old flickering arc light hung in the street almost directly in front of the hotel, and as I lay in the dark pretending to be asleep the ceiling seemed to be quivering, for the shutters fitted badly and the room could never be completely darkened. After a time I heard movement in the room, then saw a shadowy figure near the mantelpiece. I closed my eyes tightly, heard the swish of tissue paper, then the sounds of someone getting back into bed. A fog bell, blowing in the harbor and heralding bad weather, was audible.

After what seemed to me a long time I heard heavy breathing from the bed. I got up, crossed the room carefully and felt the stocking in the dark. My fingers closed on a round object in its toe. Well, I thought, one orange would be better than none.

In those days hardly any children wore pyjamas, at least not in Nova Scotia. And so a minute later, when I was sneaking down the dimly lit hall of the hotel in a white nightgown, heading for the basement stairs with the orange in my hand, I was a fairly conspicuous object. Just as I was putting my hand to the knob of the basement door I heard a tapping sound and ducked under the main stairs that led to the second floor of the hotel. The tapping came near, stopped, and I knew somebody was standing still, listening, only a few feet away.

A crisp voice said, 'You naughty boy, come out of there.'

I waited a moment and then moved into the hall. Mrs. Urquhart was standing before me in her black skirt and white cap, one hand on the handle of her cane.

'You ought to be ashamed of yourself, at this hour of the night. Go back to your room at once!'

As I went back up the hall I was afraid the noise had wakened my father. The big door creaked as I opened it and looked up at the quivering maze of shadows on the ceiling. Somebody on the bed was snoring and it seemed to be all right. I slipped into my cot and waited for several minutes, then got up again and replaced the orange in the toe of the stocking and carefully put the other gifts on top of it. As soon as I reached my cot again I fell asleep with the sudden fatigue of children.

The room was full of light when I woke up; not sunlight but the grey luminosity of filtered light reflected off snow. My parents were sitting up in bed and Chester was standing inside the door with our breakfast. My father was trying to smile under his bandages and Chester had a grin so big it showed the gap in his front teeth. The moment I had been worrying about was finally here.

The first thing I must do was display enthusiasm for my parents' sake. I went to my stocking and emptied it on my cot while Chester watched me out of the corner of his eye. Last of all the orange rolled out.

'I bet it ain't real,' Chester said.

My parents said nothing as he reached over and held it up to the light.

'No,' he said. 'It ain't real,' and dropped it on the cot again. Then he put his hand into his pocket and with an effort managed to extract a medium-sized orange. 'Look at mine,' he said. 'Look what it says right here.'

On the skin of the orange, printed daintily with someone's pen, were the words, PRODUCE OF PORTUGAL.

'So my old man's been talkin' to Santy Claus, just like Mrs. Urquhart said.'

There was never any further discussion in our family about whether Santa Claus was or was not real. Perhaps Mrs. Urquhart was the actual cause of my neurosis. I'm not a scientist, so I don't know.

HUGH MACLENNAN

Spirit
of Christmas
Present

The Crib

They are making a crêche at the Saturday morning classes
For the Christmas party: scissors and paper vie
With fingers and plasticine until there are masses
Of sheep and shepherds that kneel and stand and lie,

And cotton-batting angels with cellophane wings
And a golded cardboard star and string to guide it
And pipe-cleaner camels carrying tinfoil kings
And a real straw manger with Joseph and Mary beside it.

But the manger is empty. The Saturday classes contain
So many different faiths, there is a danger
Of giving offense; there was once no room in the inn,
Now there is no room for him in the manger.

Of course he will understand, his love is hearty
Enough to forgive and forget the being slighted
And true enough not to offend at the birthday party
By showing up where he is uninvited.

Besides he is long accustomed to the manners
Of centuries that consecrate the snub
Of Christmas honoured, not the one it honours.
Strange they should trouble to give the crêche a crib.

ROBERT FINCH

The Bachelor's Dilemma

The night before Christmas Harry Holmes, the plump young executive with the bow tie, came home to his bachelor apartment near the university and found the janitor had put a turkey on the kitchen table. It was a fine big bird weighing twenty-two pounds, far too big for his small ice box, and tied to the leg was a note from the manager of his favorite restaurant congratulating him on winning their turkey raffle. Wondering when he had taken the ticket he thought, 'Well, the devil must look after his own', and he telephoned his brother's wife who had invited him for dinner on Christmas Day. 'Well, this year, for a change I'll provide the turkey', he said, feeling exuberant. 'I've got it right here.'

'Oh, Harry, that's a shame', she said. 'We've got a turkey big enough for three days. It's in the ice box.' There was no room in the ice box for his turkey and so she had to disappoint him.

Soon he was smiling and indulging himself, anticipating the pleasure he would get giving the turkey to Tom Hill, his underpaid assistant who had just got married. Then he talked on the telephone to Tom, who had to explain his wife had bought a turkey that afternoon, and he was so apologetic and embarrassed Harry thought, 'You'd think I was trying to get him to do something for me', and he felt amused.

He called three old friends. Two were out of town for the holiday; the other had won a turkey in a bowling alley. Then he remembered that two other friends whom he admired, sports columnists on the local newspapers, were accustomed to foregathering at this hour in a cafe on Bloor Street. With the turkey in his arms he took a taxi to the cafe, grinned jovially at the hat check girl who asked him to check the turkey, strode past her to the familiar corner table, laid the turkey before his astonished friends and invited them to toss for it. One telephoned his wife, the other his sister. Both had turkeys and crowded refrigerators. The hostile waiter glared at the turkey lying on the table. And Harry's friends, having stood him treat, began to make jokes. 'I'm afraid,' one said, teasing Harry and pretending to be in the theatrical business, 'we have a turkey on our hands.' It was all very jolly, and he laughed too, but the fact was they didn't appreciate that he had thought of them, and he had to pick up his turkey and go home.

In the kitchen, standing beside the turkey, he felt irritated; it was as if his brother's wife and Tom and all his friends had joined together to deny him the satisfaction of pleasing them with a gift, and as he looked out the window at the lighted houses of his city of a million souls he suddenly felt discontented with his life which had been going so smoothly until he had to get a turkey cooked. 'There's something the matter with the world when you can't give a turkey to anyone who knows you', he thought. 'To the devil with it.'

Then he tried to sell the turkey to the restaurant, but the manager refused to buy back a turkey he had given away; 'Why don't you try a butcher?' he asked.

A butcher store a few blocks away on Harbord was still open, but the bald-headed butcher, pointing to his turkey-filled window, said, 'Look what I have left, mister! I'll sell *you* one at half price.' On the way home the big turkey seemed to take on weight, Harry's arms ached, and he was glad when he dumped it on the kitchen table. Exhausted, he lay down and fell asleep.

At the Christmas dinner at his brother's place, they were surprised to hear his turkey was still on his kitchen table, and he wondered why he felt ashamed. When he got home in the evening he stared uneasily at the naked bird. 'It'll go bad,' he thought and he sniffed. Picking it up he went out and began to cross Queen's Park. It had begun to snow. Wet dead leaves in the melting snow glistened under the park lights. Shifting the turkey from one arm to the other, he headed for a church along a side street. There he asked the white-haired man who answered the door, 'Do you know anyone who would like a Christmas turkey?' He added apologetically, 'It's late, I know'.

'It's never too late, my son', the old man said. 'I know a hundred poor families in the neighbourhood who'll appreciate a turkey. Won't you give me your name?'

'It doesn't matter,' Harry said awkwardly. And as soon as he felt the weight of the turkey being lifted off his arms he understood why he had felt ashamed at his brother's place. He hadn't been looking for someone who would appreciate a turkey. He had been looking for someone who would appreciate him.

MORLEY CALLAGHAN

The Santa Claus Parade

▲ ● ▲ ● ▲ ● ▲ ● ▲ ● ▲ ● ▲ ● ▲ ● ▲ ● ▲ ● ▲

For most of us, the Christmas season arrives almost imperceptibly; the first snow, the first decorated window, and the first 'Merry Christmas' come as a surprise, and then we start thinking of presents, parties, and Christmas pudding. Although this may be true of the absent-minded adult world, children approach the subject of Christmas with an unshakable certainty. Christmas does not sneak up on them; it arrives with tremendous fanfare on a Saturday in November. They *know* when Santa Claus is coming to town.

To the hundreds of thousands of Toronto children who line the route each year, the Santa Claus Parade marks the beginning of all the excitement, mystery, and waiting that reaches a fever pitch the moment their stocking is hung up on Christmas Eve and lasts long after the final orange is rolled out of the toe Christmas morning. Watching the Santa Claus Parade is just as much a part of Christmas as decorating the tree, roasting the turkey, and hanging up your stocking.

In spite of the November weather, which is invariably cold and bleak, or pouring with rain, in spite of the crowds and the parking problems, an estimated 500,000 people turn out to see the Parade each year, and thousands more watch it on television. The rain may leave the elegant conical hats worn by the clowns hanging limply over their ears, but it can't dampen the children's enthusiasm.

I suspect that many parents are secret Parade enthusiasts; they merely assume the role of the aloof adult who has been taken in tow by some small determined child. They may be martyrs in retrospect to their friends, but, at the time, they enjoy it as much as the children for the child's sense of wonder and magic is contagious. Even the most reluctant grown-up is caught, however briefly, in this childhood world of fantasy as he watches Cinderella in her glass slipper waiting for Prince Charming, King Arthur in gold mail and blue satin, with his two knights in shining armour on rearing steeds, and Mother Goose on her bright yellow Gander.

Inevitably this mood, precious because it is shared, is shattered by some absurd, insistent question.

'No dear, that's not the Queen of Tarts, that's the Queen of Hearts,' the adult explains patiently.

'But why? The Queen made some tarts all-on-a-summer's-day, so why isn't she the Queen of Tarts?'

'Well, she's not.'

'But she didn't make any hearts, did she?'

The discussion becomes very involved. By this time the giant papier mâché figure of the Queen of Hearts, in her red, ermine-trimmed cape, blue gown and golden crown has almost disappeared. Only the large red satin heart, flanked by flowers which forms the back of the float is still visible. Meanwhile Old King Cole with his Fiddlers Three, his Pipe and his Bowl on a magenta, pink and red float, Goldilocks, and Robin Hood have passed by unnoticed. Even St. George with his fire-breathing dragon fails to distract the child from his questioning. Finally the hoof-beats of the horses drawing Peter Pumpkin-Eater's Coach catch his ear and once more he becomes absorbed in the Parade.

The Parade is carefully thought out and planned to appeal to a child's imagination. Colours, costumes, and floats are skilfully co-ordinated to produce a harmonious whole. Clowns and carnival heads are designed to amuse the children. 'To a child, anything that is out of proportion is funny, outsize feet and enormous buttons, for example,' says Mr. Jack Brockie, creator of the Parade. 'But we deliberately avoid anything grotesque or horrifying. One year we had long, wiggly serpents, which might have frightened the children, so we gave them long, curling eye-lashes. We want to evoke the child's sense of wonderment, not to frighten him. At the same time we have to be realistic. Children are very discerning; King Arthur must look like a knight, not a cowboy.'

Mr. Brockie has worked on the Parade almost since its inception in Toronto in 1905. Over the years he has watched it grow until to-day there are four Santa Claus Parades across Canada. The entire Toronto Parade, complete with floats, carnival heads and costumes, is shipped to Montreal and repeated a week later. Winnipeg and Edmonton now have their own Parades on a smaller scale, but Toronto remains the home of the original Santa Claus Parade.

Down through the years Santa has made spectacular entrances to the city in almost every type of float, in a chariot, gleaming with sword-like icicles, in a huge aeroplane, aboard a truck, astride a silver fish, on an iceberg drawn by polar bears, in the caboose of an engine, but none has thrilled the children as much as Santa sitting in his sleigh with those famous eight white reindeer leaping over star-dust clouds. 'As long as I am in charge of the Parade,' says Mr. Brockie, 'Santa Claus will arrive in a sleigh with eight reindeer, you know, the whole Night-Before-Christmas bit.' In creating the Santa Claus Parade, he has made a myth into an institution.

Tradition plays a significant role in the design of the Parade as a whole. Science has managed through fiction, radio, press and television to send the minds of children soaring into space. The people who plan the Parade, 'wise in the ways of children and grown-ups,' have kept rockets, planets, and missiles completely divorced from Santa's Parade. Hundreds of thousands of people watch the Parade every year. Why? Because they know the theme will be a familiar one, the Storybook characters they have known and loved from childhood. When grandfather stands beside his daughter and they point out the characters to a small grandson, a family bond is being strengthened and the Christmas Spirit, as well as Santa Claus, has indeed been brought to town.

The first Santa Claus Parade in 1905 was a very modest affair. Santa arrived at the Union Station and rode through the downtown streets on a checkered red and black packing case set on a wagon drawn by a team of horses. The following year he arrived with considerably more flourish in a Tally-ho drawn by four white horses, with two footmen and two trumpeters to herald his coming. By 1909 Santa was mechanized and accompanied by a circus band.

The next three years the Parade started from Newmarket on a Friday afternoon, stopped overnight at York Mills, and proceeded down Yonge Street on Saturday afternoon. It was a long ride for Santa, sitting on candy canes or squeezed into the chimney of a log cabin with only an oil stove to keep him from freezing.

1913 was a memorable year. Santa drove down Yonge Street from the North Toronto Station in a sled led by eight tiny live reindeer. They had been brought all the way from Labrador with a special supply of moss for food and a veterinary to look after them. Men dressed in lion, bear, and tiger skins walked beside the timid animals who shied at the sight of these make-believe beasts. Periodically the parade would halt and children would gather around the sled to sing while the band played. They also tossed letters for Santa into a large net basket attached to a long pole carried by a bearer. Every one of the thousands of letters was answered.

In 1916 the Royal Court which Santa held throughout the Christmas season was moved from Massey Hall to a Toyland set up in Eaton's store. The royal retinue now boasted seven floats, Cinderella in her Pumpkin Coach, the Old Woman in the Shoe, Miss Muffet on her Tuffet, Little Boy Blue, Little Bo Peep, Mother Goose and Little Red Riding Hood. The largest float was a huge swan with a band of musicians, clowns and Santa in the midst of it all.

Each year the Parade has become more lavish; and production is now a year-round project. Ideas for next year's Parade are on the drawing board before this year's Parade is on the road. Early in January, Mr. Brockie meets with the designers to decide on plans for the new Parade. As soon as the blueprints are ready, permanent staff and carpenters begin the construction of new floats and the redecoration of old ones; the artists and designers start making fairies, glass slippers, swans and papier mâché heads; the costume designers start creating a new wardrobe. In October bands and marchers are organized, and the last sequin is sewn in place. Many years of experience have brought the production of the Parade to a peak of mechanical perfection. Even so there is the occasional hitch. One year Santa almost drove off without any batteries for the loudspeakers on his sleigh. Near panic broke out, until someone thought of 'borrowing' two batteries from a nearby car. How could Santa drive around Queen's Park without his Ho Ho Ho?

MARGARET MUNNOCH

Our First Canadian Christmas

Very soon now it will be Christmas Eve, the fifth Christmas we have spent in Canada. We are among the one million new Canadians who at this nostalgic and sentimental time of the year must blend the traditions of a lifetime with the unfamiliar sounds, atmosphere and smells of a Canadian Christmas.

My husband, our two children and I have learned to love this country with a passion that embarrasses our Canadian friends. We learned the splendor of living here on the eve of our first Christmas in Canada and each Christmas since has been a milestone in a new and marvellous life. Every year we accept more of the tradition and gaiety of the Canadian Christmas. But I hope I won't sound like an ungrateful guest if I mention a little later in this article a disturbing element in the Canadian Christmas, an element to which we can never become accustomed . . .

Two days after I arrived in Toronto I found a night job in a candy factory wrapping Christmas candy canes. I approached this job with trepidation. I knew of the efficiency of Canadian factory workers and I despaired of holding the job. I spoke little English and one of the girls showed me how to roll the Cellophane wrapper around the candy cane in sign language.

After a few hours there was a break for lunch, but I had brought none. One of the girls approached me and indicated she had too many sand-wiches. 'Help me eat them, please,' she said. I shared her lunch and the other workers sat around me and told me the English words 'bread' and 'water'.

The next months were the same. For two weeks, until I began bring-ing my own lunch, someone always had too many sandwiches and I 'helped' them. While we ate I would recite the new English words I had learned the night before and the girls would teach me more. They were delighted at my progress.

That's when I fell in love with Canada. No one had told those people in the factory how to behave toward a stranger. They knew I needed kindness and love and they gave it to me. When the Christmas candy was finished and there was no longer any work for me, the boss called me into his office and showed real concern for my future. He knew nothing about me and I could scarcely talk with him because of my poor English, but he wrote me a letter of recommendation complimenting me so highly that I wept. If I had to give up either my university diploma or that letter of recommendation, I would hand over the diploma without hesitation. It is a wonderful letter.

They told me at the factory that the Christmas decorations in Union Station are beautiful. Because I had no money or time to prepare a Christmas tree for my children—I was making only fifteen dollars a week—I decided to take them to Union Station on Christmas Eve.

The station was lovely beyond description. Around us were towering trees filled with colored lights and the high vaulted ceiling above us gave me the feeling of being in a church. I held Peter, who was nearly two, and Nadine stood beside me. I began to pray and Nadine, thinking of home and her father, wiped tears from her eyes.

A couple approached us. The man was big and white-haired and smoking a cigar. Peter later called it a piece of wood because he had never seen a cigar. The woman was pink-complexioned, wore glasses and also had white hair. They looked at my twelve-year-old daughter wiping her eyes.

'Have you lost something?' asked the man kindly.

'No, no,' I assured him. 'It's nothing. It's our first Christmas in Canada and she is missing her father.'

The couple went away and in a moment returned with candy, giftwrapped in a Christmas paper. For Peter there was a small rubber soldier. They put the parcels in the children's hands, said 'Merry Christmas' and disappeared again before I could thank them.

I don't think it will sound sacrilegious if I say that for the only time in my life I had the feeling that Jesus had come to earth. There are words like humanity and brotherhood for it, but by themselves they don't convey enough. How can you be lost in a country that has such people?

The following Christmas my husband was with us. He had arrived early in June, still a sick and broken man as a result of those three months of torture. I had found him a job on a farm, where we thought the sunshine and fresh air would help him, and he had to leave for it the next day. We said hello to him one day and good-by the next. It was very hard.

After he had worked on the farm for a while he came back to the city and took a job in a lumberyard.

The day before our second Christmas in Canada Zdenko came into the apartment with a Scotch pine. 'Children,' he called, 'I want to introduce you to a Canadian Christmas tree. Canadian Christmas tree, meet the Hradsky children.' We never had a Scotch pine before, only fir and spruce.

Christmas in Czechoslovakia is very different from Christmas in Canada. Our Santa Claus is Saint Nicholas, a proud and dignified bishop in white and gold. He knocks on the door the evening of December 6 and comes in carrying a white sack with a gold crest. Behind him is a small hunched figure in black fur with a broom and a black bag. The children are waiting in a dim, candlelit room. If they have been good, Saint Nicholas gives them apples and nuts painted gold; if they haven't behaved, the black figure, which represents the devil, gives them a piece of coal and a spank with the broom. I have never known a child who hadn't been good—well, pretty good.

That night the shoes the children have been polishing all day are put on the window sill with a pair of socks and the next morning the shoes and socks are filled with candies and apples and nuts.

Christmas itself is reserved for reverence and the warmth of family love. The twenty-fourth of December is a fasting day for both Protestants and Catholics. I know about this because we have both religions in our family: my husband and son are Catholic and my daughter and I are Protestant. Naturally, the family goes as a group to both churches.

During the day of the twenty-fourth most people are too excited to eat anyway. We eat only soup, made from butter and flour browned in a pan with water added and bread. Some people only drink tea. In the afternoon we go to church. As it grows dusk the children press their faces against the window and watch for the first star. Just as they see it, a silver bell rings somewhere in the house and doors are opened to a room that has been closed all day. Inside there are no lights but the candles on the Christmas tree. Under the tree is the manger with the image of the baby Jesus in it, wrapped in the family's best lace. The family kneels around the tree and the youngest child, the one closest in age to the Babe, begins to pray. After that the family sings Christmas hymns. The room smells of burning candles and pine; I believed for years that Jesus brought the tree, in remembrance of His birthday. There is a feeling of holiness around it.

Afterward there is the family supper. A Catholic family has soup and then carp, which is known in Czechoslovakia as the Christmas fish, and buttered potatoes. The dessert, called *lokse,* has been blessed in the church. It is made of long loaves, dried and cut in pieces which are then soaked in milk and honey. A paste of poppy seeds and syrup is made and the bread is pressed into the paste. When it is served it is thin and crisp and covered with honey.

The Protestants have a soup made of the water from sauerkraut, mixed with browned butter and flour. Dried mushrooms and pieces of meat are added and sour cream is put on top. It's called *kapustnica* and we make thirty or forty portions at a time. It's served several times during the Christmas week and by New Year's it is at its best. After the soup and carp, some families have Christmas turkey. Western-minded Czechoslovakians were beginning to prefer turkey to the usual chicken before I left.

Christmas morning everyone sleeps in and breakfast is late. Each family has prepared special Christmas pastries, filled with poppy seeds and nuts. Around noon everyone begins to visit friends and relatives and a home-made drink called *briata* is served. It's made from pure alcohol with burnt sugar, caramel and spices, and is light and aromatic.

Our second Christmas in Canada, when my husband was with us, I set out to duplicate the food we associate with Christmas. I bought five tins of sauerkraut to get enough water for the soup and I had a difficult time finding a carp. I found I couldn't make *lokse* at all, so I bought French bread and toasted pieces of it and no one complained. This year I think I will have to make a change in the menu. I'll buy salmon or halibut for the Christmas fish. My family says that they don't think carp is a delicacy at all any more.

At four o'clock on Christmas Eve we took my husband to Union Station. We have done this every Christmas Eve since and I think many new Canadians do the same. We see dozens of pale faces with their eyes turned to the sky and we know that, like us, they are praying.

We went back to the apartment and I rang the little bell, though it was not silver, and we stood around the tree and looked at the manger. We had replaced the candles with Canadian electric lights which are much safer, but otherwise it was the same. That year the children sang carols in English, while we listened with pride. Afterward we had some gifts for them, ballet slippers and a pullover for Nadine and a coat and leggings set for Peter. I had been paying for that outfit for three months, sometimes only a quarter a week. My husband paid off the difference and put the outfit under the tree as a present from me. Peter looked like a young prince in it . . .

Sometimes, when I speak to groups like the IODE, I tell of the marvel of our first Christmas Eve in Union Station but I never mention the part of the Canadian Christmas that distresses me. It seems to us that Canadians have changed the emphasis of Christmas from the birthday of Jesus to Santa Claus. The poetry of that little Babe in the manger is so beautiful I can't understand this. Children here realize perfectly the meaning of Easter but seem unaware of the meaning of Christmas.

We think that a child can best begin to learn about religion by appreciating that Jesus too was a child like themselves. It is a consolation for poor children to know that the Highest Spirit was also poor. I didn't know that most of my life, but I know it now.

Everywhere you look in Canada at this time of the year you see Santa Claus. I was horrified last year when Peter got Santa Claus and Jesus mixed. We were just coming off a department-store escalator as the Santa Claus passed by and kindly rubbed Peter's head.

'I'm blessed!' cried Peter in ecstasy. 'I'll never wash my hair again. He bless me!'

He had transferred his holy admiration for Jesus to this nice ho-ho man and we had to fight to bring the manger into focus again. I can't see how Santa Claus can help you with your troubles when you grow up.

DR. NADINE HRADSKY

Social Engineering

★ ★ ★ ★ ★ ★ ★ ★ ★ ★ ★ ★ ★ ★ ★ ★ ★ ★ ★

In all our cities and most of the bigger towns, Santa Claus is now bray-ing, ho-hoing and singing his infernal ditties out of store windows, over the top of transoms, and from other points of vantage and surprise all over the downtown districts. It is to continue for another sixteen days. The question is: can we take it.?

Santa Claus originally was a secretive sort of fellow. Not only did nobody ever see him. You weren't even supposed to hear him. He came by stealth in the middle of the night. So intent upon not being visualized was he that he came down chimneys instead of using doors or even windows. A more elusive and invisible character did not exist. He was such stuff as dreams are made on, and you were only to see him in your dreams.

Then along about the three-quarter post of the last century, some-body, probably a merchant at that, or a salesman, got the idea of dress-ing up as Santa Claus in his own house, and entertaining his children. The idea spread like wildfire. Santa Claus suits and beards went on sale everywhere. By 1900, a daddy who wouldn't dress up as Santa Claus early Christmas morning wasn't worthy of the name.

But just about the time every house on the street had an old Santa Claus outfit stowed away with the Christmas decorations, the stores got the notion of removing the old gentleman from the domestic to the mercantile sphere. And there he is today, dozens of him in every city, as competitive an old boy as ever came out of mythology.

The conversion of Santa Claus from the most elusive and ethereal into the most solid and multiple of figures, all within two generations, is probably as slick a job as the twentieth century has done so far. From a soundless wraith into the noisiest guy in history it stands as quite a feat of social engineering.

GREGORY CLARK

Yule Logging

♠ ♠ ♠ ♠ ♠ ♠ ♠ ♠ ♠ ♠ ♠ ♠ ♠ ♠ ♠ ♠ ♠ ♠ ♠

It is a lamentable fact that there are many common misconceptions about Christmas trees, not the least of which is that they are necessary. 'Christmas isn't Christmas without a tree,' somebody says—somebody who never went through the arboreal nightmare of putting one up, somebody who never went to bed Christmas eve with pitch on his hands and pine needles down his neck, somebody, in short, who ought to keep his big fat mouth shut.

Highly significant is the fact that the custom of dragging a young forest into the living room the third week in every December originated in Germany, home of so many other secret weapons and inhuman engines of torture. The good old English custom was to hang a stocking over the fireplace. Anybody can hang a stocking over a fireplace. All you need is a stocking, a fireplace, a wad of gum, and you're set. But, no. Because the Germans were hauling coniferous headaches into their homes, we had to get in on it. We got trees, too, we said, with fierce national pride, and began the mad chopping and hacking and hammering that has continued to the present day.

The commercial advantages of Christmas trees soon became apparent to manufacturers. Unless there is something seriously wrong with your calves, you can get more presents under a tree than you can in your stocking. Try inserting a wagon, a frigidaire, or a set of golf clubs in the average cotton sock (no fair forcing or shoving), and you realize immediately why big business is solidly behind the Christmas tree, with its arm around Lucifer's shoulders.

Well, cornered by Teuton sabotage, the greed of vested interests and the persistent whining of the family, you have no choice but to erect a Christmas tree. As though you don't have trouble enough staggering into the house Christmas eve, after snifting a few with the boys at the office, you have to tangle suddenly with this stand of timber in the hall, an encounter likely as not to persuade you that you have missed the entrance to the house altogether and are flailing about in the garden shrubbery.

But let us not anticipate all the fun and gladness that a Christmas tree carries in every green, bushy, eye-gouging branch. The first decision you must make, after putting it off until Santa Claus has his leg cocked over the chimney, is whether you will buy a tree or go forth into the woods and hew your own. If you have a taste for the romantic, if you feel imbued with the true, rousing Christmas spirit, and especially if you are something of a congenital idiot, you will elect to hew.

With the song of the woodsman on your lips, you sling your tiny kindling hatchet across your shoulder and strike out along the path leading to the garage. From there you continue the journey by car, nosing into the country, staring out the side-window for a fir or pine that will go on top of the radio without requiring a major alteration in the roof. You meet other cars whose drivers are doing exactly the same thing. Womp. You compare damage to fenders and headlights, and even a rough estimate of the repair bill promises to exceed the price of a boughten tree by a week's salary.

Gripping your hatchet a bit tighter than necessary, you stalk into the woods with a seasonal snarl in your throat. Three bogs and a slightly sprained ankle later, you find the tree you want. It's a beauty. The part you covet starts about sixty feet above the ground, but it's worth it. Fiercely you attack the trunk with the hatchet and soon the chips are flying, a remarkably high percentage of them straight into your good eye. Half-way through, both you and the hatchet lose your heads and you continue in a cold fury with pocket-knife, teeth, and brutal kicks from all sides, occasionally jumping on this symbol of Yuletide joy and trying to claw it down.

Waiting patiently at the car as you emerge trailing your kill is a man whose bearing and sidearms are those of an official of the government. You can't help wondering, when you note the expression on his face, whether there might be something in the sign reading 'PROVINCIAL REFORESTATION PROJECT—CUT NO TREES'. Sure enough, stocked with a pass from this gentleman to your favourite neighbourhood police court, you make for home with your tree, which is rapidly becoming a pain in the lumbar region.

You haul the tree into the living room, carefully ignoring the family's ill-timed observations about the scrawniness of its lower branches, and try it for size on top of the radio. After you have, in cold blood, cut the legs off the radio, the treetop's tinsel star of Bethlehem continues to ride along the ceiling at a rakish angle, but you don't want to hear any more about it, see. You've had a hard day, Christmas or no Christmas, you can't help feeling that dogs have the right attitude towards trees.

After a restless night haunted by dreams of having to chop your way out of the Black Forest with a butter knife, you start the next evening to hang the coloured lights on the tree. For sheer, noisy fun, this is the next best thing to a strike riot or a South American revolution.

First, with the judicious eye of the artist, you weave the strings of lights through the branches until they lie just right. You insert the wall plug. Do the lights come to life in brilliant blues, greens and reds, transforming the tree into a miracle of colour? Not quite. Not just yet. In fact they sit there as though they had never heard of Edison. The only difference is that if you touch them now you stand a fair chance of being electrocuted. Somewhere among those dozens of little bulbs there is a dud, or several duds, and the game is to find which it is without calling in the General Electric Company. Any number of people can play this game, but only one ever does, you great big beautiful sucker, you. While your fingers fumble from socket to socket, testing each bulb with what you like to think is a good bulb, various other members of the family stand around throwing imitation snow at the tree in-accurately, so that you have inhaled several acres of cotton before you realize why your breathing is becoming laboured.

Some hours later you have successfully removed the strings of lights from the tree, hammered all the bulbs to a fine powder, and stamped downtown to buy an entirely new set.

Once again the tree is ready. You plug in the lights and delight to see the old evergreen break into gobs of warm colour.

'Come look at the tree,' you holler to the rest of the family. 'Or I'll break every bone in your heads.'

The family thumps in, eager to be dazzled. They are—by your beet face.

'You'll have to move faster than that!' you roar, waving a quivering hand at the darkened tree. 'How long d'ya expect these lights to last—forever?'

At last, on Christmas eve, the tree stands complete, a cheerful picture waiting for Santa to bring his presents. The kiddies go to bed, to be awakened in the middle of the night by a hideous crash, above which they can hear Mommy yelling 'Timber!' In the morning, seeing the tree slouching, dejected and lightless, they ask:

'What happened, Mommy? Did Santa knock the tree over tying on a present?'

'He tied one on, all right,' murmurs Mommy drily.

'What's that present Daddy's wearing, Mommy?'

'Two of Santa's helpers in white coats brought that, darling. Doesn't Daddy look handsome in his lovely new strait jacket?'

'Just what I needed,' giggles Daddy. 'No Tiny Tim is complete without one. Ha ha ha ha . . .'

E. P. NICOL

Contractual Goodwill

Many people complain, and justly so, about the commercialized Christmas. Perhaps it is time to note the emergence of something just as dreary—the contractual, or collectively bargained, Christmas. An instance of this latter is to be found in the evidence submitted to the conciliation board which visited Hamilton to investigate the dispute between the Steel Company of Canada and the United Steel Workers. In 1950, the company agreed to pay all of its employees a day's pay for Christmas Day, and waive all of the qualifying clauses of the statutory holiday section of its collective agreement. Two years later, it agreed to include statutory holiday allowance hours as time worked in computing overtime. This led to discussions about Christmas Day, as a result of which (according to the company's brief):

'It was mutually agreed that where an employee received a Christmas Day allowance and was normally scheduled to work on that day, then those hours would be included as hours worked for the purpose of computing overtime. On the other hand, if the employee received the Christmas Day allowance, but was not normally scheduled to work on Christmas Day, in other words received the allowance as a gift, then the Christmas Day allowance hours under these circumstances would not be included in computing overtime. The union has asked that this interpretation be included in the collective agreement.'

Far be it from us to argue the rights and wrongs of this complicated dispute. We merely remark that it seems a long way removed from the Christmas of the holly and mistletoe; and a still longer way removed from the Christmas of the shepherds and the Wise Men. Peace in Stelco, we hope; good-will towards the Ontario Labor Relations Board. But nobody is going to get a carol out of it.

GLOBE & MAIL

A Cricket Singing

▲ ▲

On this Christmas Day I am to tell you something about the seasonal doings of animals and birds in Canada. With our migrant birds on coasts that feel the sun, with many animals asleep in dark chambers underground, with the tide of wild life at low ebb, it might be reasonably inferred that there is a dearth of news of interest concerning creatures of the Canadian wilderness. But such is not the case. From the sea coasts, the forests, the prairie and the mountains there are so many pertinent news items about the furred and feathered inhabitants that frankly, I am perplexed.

Suppose I begin by telling you about a midget. The smallest mammal in the whole world is the shrew, a tiny mouse-like creature with a pointed snout, brown teeth and a somewhat square tail. Shrews are present in enormous numbers in all provinces of Canada, in the North West Territories and in the Yukon. Few if any of these diminutive beasts now alive will see the dawn of another Christmas, yet each one today ate at least four Christmas dinners. The shrew has a very short life, being almost in dotage on its first birthday and seldom surviving more than one winter. It might well be called the Hardy Annual of the animal world. Yet though this minute creature has been granted only a pittance of days, it contrives to crowd the hours of a brief existence, living at high speed and, for its size, consuming immense quantities of food. Having a very high blood temperature possibly 108 or 110 degrees, and an extremely rapid digestion, it is imperative that a shrew should eat at least once in every two hours. Lacking sustenance for a longer period it will die of starvation. The shrew is dependent on grubs and beetles for winter food, most of the waking hours being spent in hasty search for dormant forms of insect life concealed under the carpet of the forest and the tundra. It is a pugnacious fighter, spoiling for contest with others of its kind and capable of throttling a field mouse three times its size and weight. While nearly all shrews come to a natural and peaceful end, yet strange to say none die in bed. Closely related to the mole, the shrew is likewise obscure in life but when the

DAN McCOWAN

last sleep time comes, it, in common with the mole, emerges from cover and lies down beneath the wide and starry sky.

The evergreen forests of Canada are silent with the snow this Christmas Day. Small flocks of grosbeaks and crossbills, birds especially equipped for extracting seeds from the cones of spruce and fir trees, flit hither and thither in the tall green steeples. The white coverlet on open spaces in the woods bears clear imprint of the feathery feet of walking grouse, of the wing tip of the Horned Owl or of the short deep furrow ploughed by a porcupine as it waddled from the base of one pine tree to another. The dinner of this formidable yet peaceable animal consisted today of a simple salad of the inner bark of an ever-green tree, a food more filling than satisfying, but which nevertheless in time of famine has proved a lifesaver to many a spiny pig and many a starving Indian. I am convinced that a Canadian porcupine in winter-time exists on a modicum of food obtained with the minimum of effort. An individual has been known to remain aloft in one tree continuously for a fortnight.

Such a lethargic mode of life must seem strange to the industrious bustling woodpeckers, birds which are obliged to work hard and for long hours in order to gain a livelihood. They did not have even a half holiday today but were continuously employed in scanning the tree bark for torpid insects, in hewing and gouging into holes which harbour wood-borers, and in probing all cracks and crannies wherein grubs might be concealed. These feathered foresters, working not on salary but on commission only, are well equipped for the business in hand. The claws, the tail, the bill, the tongue and the shock absorber in the neck have all been specially developed for the purpose of coping with an army of grubs and worms which, lacking control, would speedily lay waste the great forests of this Dominion. So the woodpeckers had a busy Christmas Day and tonight all are asleep, not perched on bare branches exposed to the north wind, but sheltered within small chambers hollowed in the trunks of trees.

The wild goats of Canada live in penthouses on top of the mountains in Alberta, in British Columbia and in the Yukon. These lofty habi-tations are thoroughly air-conditioned but not very well heated. Consequently the shaggy tenants on Christmas Day, as well as on all other days of winter, keep warm by climbing up and down the stairs of the limestone terraces, the while browsing small herbage and scraping leathery lichens from the rocks for food. They are all clad in white woolly coats and baggy white trousers. The grandfathers and grandmothers wear Santa Claus beards which serve nicely as mufflers on a frosty morning. Both young and old are furnished with sole rubbers to keep them from slipping on the snowy rocks. They could easily descend to the lower and more sheltered wooded slopes but prefer to remain up in cloudland where they are not menaced by the cougar or wolverine and where the great winds sweep the snow from small plants on which they depend for food. Up there no rain falls in winter to soak them to the skin and chill them to the marrow. Falling snow is easily shaken from the coat and thus, while mountain goats apparently suffer from either rheumatism or a form of 'housemaid's knee', I have never known one to have a cold in the head.

During summer the goats have neighbours such as the Grey Crowned Rosy Finch, a small bird which nests on the topmost towers of the Rockies and feeds its young on a chowder of frozen insects. Another acquaintance of the goat in summer is the marmot or Whistler. Neither Rosy Finch nor marmot piped 'Happy Christmas' to the woolly goats today; the finch was far south—the marmot deep in the ground. In fact the marmot, a grand-uncle of the woodchuck, retires for the winter some time about Labour Day and spending almost seven months in a 'somnolent posture' knows nothing of Thanksgiving, Christmas or Easter. To the marmot every day of summer is a 'tag day' when he is likely to be held up by a swooping eagle or pinned down by a sneaking weasel. Small wonder that when autumn comes the marmot obtains long leave of absence, soothing his jittery nerves in a profound sleep.

Few birds are visible on Christmas Day on the prairies of Canada. The Robins and bluebirds are down in the peanut fields of Virginia; the meadowlark also went south with his flute some time ago and most of the waterfowl hatched in Saskatchewan are today paddling in the still lagoons of Florida. Members of the grouse family, old-timers in the West, are permanent residents of the plains and capable of finding board and lodging even in the bleakest winter weather. The prairie-chicken, clucking its way through the willow scrub, plucked buds from the twigs for dinner today. Tonight if the weather is moderate, it will sleep in the lee of a windrow of tumble-weed or rumple its feathers in a small coulee. When fierce winds sweep across the stubble fields, driving the snow in hissing clouds, these resourceful birds seek shelter in the drifts. Diving headlong into deep snowbanks they are out of the wind, protected from the frost and concealed from the eye and nose of the hungry coyote.

Today if a coyote were in luck it had one meal; if not, it hoped for better things tomorrow. There must be many meatless days for these small wolves in winter—days when grouse are wary and nights when rabbits cannot be ambushed. I am convinced that if a coyote has its meal ticket punched but twelve times in the course of one winter, it will continue to yodel cheerfully and live to welcome the gophers in the spring.

Across the Arctic wilderness of Canada, almost within shadow of the Pole, two hardy birds contrive to exist through the cold dark days of winter. One of these birds has permanent coal-black plumage; the other is temporarily clad in white. The sombre bird is the raven, the snowy one the Rock Ptarmigan. In quest of food on Christmas Day the raven, as on every other day of the year, makes many aerial surveys of the barren lands. An habitual camp follower of the wolf pack, it watches eagerly for a chance to partake of the small fragments remaining from the carcass of a caribou that has fallen victim to the wild dogs of of the north. The ptarmigan, a species of grouse, is a vegetarian, living on the buds and berries of dwarf shrubs. When searching for food it normally does so on foot. During summer it goes barefoot but in winter it requires snowshoes. These are provided by a seasonal growth of feathers on the toes, enabling the wearer to walk securely on the surface of the deep snow.

In remote valleys of the Selkirks and the Rockies one little bird sings carols today. A persistent vocalist is the Water Ouzel or Dipper, piping a roundelay in December as in June. Apparently unwilling to broadcast without a musical accompaniment this happy bird resorts to a little waterfall or to the margin of a brook where the water tinkles melodiously amongst the mossy stones, and there sings a solo to the bending willows and curtsies to the standing trees. The chickadees in all parts of Canada chirped blithely today as they hung from the horizontal bars of the birches or scanned the slender poplar twigs in search of food. I imagine that these plump birds must particularly enjoy Christmas Day, for the small groups seen in winter are usually formed of members of one family remaining in company through summer and autumn and until spring.

Most of the Red Squirrels did their Christmas shopping in October. This afternoon, those that were awake came downstairs from the mossy nest to munch a few nuts or seeds stored carefully in the cellar. Dried mushrooms may also have been on the bill of fare of squirrels today. The fungi are collected by the animals in sunny autumn weather and placed high on branches of the trees where they are quickly sun-cured and where they remain in good condition until wanted. Deer and marmots and porcupines are also fond of mushrooms but they have not discovered how such food may be preserved for winter use.

Beavers ate pickled poplar bark today, while muskrats dined off succulent roots of water plants. The herons, tall stream-lined birds stalking stealthily in the tidal shallow, spent the day in spearing fish. Kingfishers went marketing this morning for sprats. Gulls and crows wintering on our coasts had shell-fish for dinner. Snow buntings all across the prairies gathered good seed for breakfast. High in the Rockies contented conies nibbled fragrant hay from the stacks which they prudently built in mellow days of autumn.

Good Sirs and Ladies all, I pray that on your hearth tonight a cricket may be singing merrily.

DAN McCOWAN

3   4   5   Alg   76